Acknowledgments

Dr. Armand Hammer is a man for whom the impossible
is natural and from whom the unexpected is expected.
Yet the development of his collection from the time of
its first public exhibition only two years ago is still
astonishing. At that time the collection numbered
seventy-nine works, most of them European paintings
and drawings from Corot to Chagall. Today
the collection is almost double that number. In 1969
there were no drawings earlier than the Boudin of
1869. Today the old master drawings in the collection,
including works of the rarest masters, Raphael and
Dürer, would do honor to a veteran connoisseur of
drawings. Two years ago the collection included
only one American painting, the Sargent portrait
of Mrs. Edward Livingston Davis and her son;
today there is a distinguished group of Americans
from Gilbert Stuart to Andrew Wyeth. In the field of
concentration of the collection, the nineteenth and
early twentieth century, master works of Moreau,
Pissarro, Monet, Degas, Renoir, van Gogh,
and Cézanne have been added.

From this augmented collection, John Walker,
Director Emeritus of the National Gallery of Art
in Washington, has selected for exhibition at the
Royal Academy in London, the National Gallery of
Ireland, and the Los Angeles County Museum of Art
those works which he believes best represent
Dr. Hammer's taste and intention. Dr. Hammer's
objective in collecting is to bring together works of art
which he feels have a special aesthetic significance
and meaning to the American people today and
to share them with the people. The sincerity of
his intention is demonstrated by the fact that
during the past two years Dr. Hammer's collection
has been shown in whole or in part in Memphis,
Washington, Kansas City, Columbus, New Orleans,
Little Rock, Oklahoma City, San Francisco, and

San Diego, that is, not only in the large metropolitan museums which might enhance the prestige of the collection but also in the smaller institutions whose visitors might not frequently have the chance to see paintings and drawings by the masters represented in it.

The catalog notes were prepared for the most part by the staff of the Los Angeles County Museum of Art: Ebria Feinblatt, the drawings; Charles Millard, the nineteenth- and early twentieth-century European paintings; Larry Curry, the American paintings; I prepared the entries for the old master paintings. The notes on the Raphael and Dürer drawings were written by Dr. Konrad Oberhuber, formerly of the Albertina Graphics Collection, Vienna, and now Research Curator of Drawings at the National Gallery in Washington; that on the Géricault portrait by Professor Lorenz Eitner of Stanford University; and that on the Rembrandt drawing by Dr. Christopher White, formerly of the staff of the British Museum and recently appointed Curator of Prints of the National Gallery of Art in Washington, who is preparing an additional publication of the drawing. Edward Cornachio took the color transparencies. Jeanne Doyle and Joanne Jaffe followed the editing, designing, and production from manuscript to final book.

Our debts of gratitude are many: to John Walker and Denys Sutton, editor of *Apollo* magazine, for their introductory essays; to Dr. Oberhuber, Dr. Eitner, and Dr. White for their catalog entries; to Mrs. Elizabeth Andrews, who furnished much of the documentation; to Carolyn H. Wells, Research Assistant to John Walker, who painstakingly reviewed the entries in the earlier Hammer catalogs at the Library of Congress; to Victor Hammer for his ready cooperation; and to Carl Blumay who worked with our editorial staff through the entire production of the catalog.

Our deepest gratitude, of course, is owed Dr. and Mrs. Armand Hammer for allowing us to present their collection to the people of Los Angeles and to the many young visitors from Southern California and across the country we expect here during the holiday season.

Kenneth Donahue

Director, Los Angeles County Museum of Art

The Armand Hammer Collection

Los Angeles County
Museum of Art
December 21, 1971-February 27, 1972

Royal Academy of Arts
London
June 24-July 24, 1972

National Gallery of Ireland
Dublin
August 9-October 1, 1972

Library of Congress
Catalog Card Number 73-184668

Copyrighted (c) 1971 by
Museum Associates of the
Los Angeles County Museum of Art

I.S.B.N. 0-87587-047-3

Published by the
Los Angeles County Museum of Art

Preface

I once asked Armand Hammer why he collected.
"Because it's fun!" he explained. "It's a hunt. I get a
certain joy out of finding rare works, out of learning
the stories attached to them. I've always liked to collect.
I used to collect stamps. My father had a great stamp
collection. But pictures are something more than just
collecting. You are connecting yourself with something
that really is immortal, something that has survived all
these centuries. You are preserving something
for posterity."

Armand Hammer is a doctor of medicine although he
has never practiced. He received his degree from the
Columbia Medical School, studying at night and in the
daytime running a family pharmaceutical company.
The family firm was on the verge of bankruptcy, but he
made it so profitable that on graduation he had a clear
profit of one million dollars.

While waiting to begin his internship at the Bellevue
Medical Center, he decided in 1921 to go to Russia
whence his grandfather had emigrated, and to use his
medical knowledge and a field hospital he had
purchased to combat typhus, which was raging in the
Urals. He found, however, when after many difficulties
he got to the Russian interior, that though typhus was
everywhere, the real enemy was starvation. The famine
he saw struck him, as he said, "with cold horror." He
decided to use a substantial part of his capital to
eliminate the terrible shortage of food. He entered into
an agreement with the local Soviet that he buy a million
bushels of American wheat, which he estimated would
feed the local population until their own crops,
destroyed by a combination of drought and Revolution,
were once more harvestable. He stipulated, however,
that the ships bringing the grain be filled with Russian
goods which could be sold in the United States, so that
the food supply could be replenished.

When Lenin heard of this, he asked to meet this

young American, who at twenty-three had become a hero in the Urals. The meeting between the two was an immediate success. They became and remained firm friends. Lenin proposed that Armand Hammer accept one or more Soviet concessions. After thinking over the offer, he decided to choose two, one for mining asbestos, which proved minimally profitable, and the second for an export-import business, which succeeded beyond his most sanguine hopes. He represented eventually thirty-seven leading American companies, and he was the first to import Fordson tractors, thus beginning the mechanization of Russian agriculture.

He settled down in Moscow and spent the next nine years in the Soviet Union. Needing a residence, he rented an unfurnished palace, and decorating it gave him his first interest in art. His younger brother, Victor, who had studied art history at Princeton, became Armand's tutor. Together they bought for next to nothing eighteenth-century French furniture, Aubusson rugs, services of Sèvres china, Meissen porcelains, all the household furnishings which were sold in Commission Stores where such treasures were brought by the impoverished aristocracy and even the middle class.

Around 1928 a New York art dealer, seeing the bargains the Hammer brothers were picking up, offered a partnership in his firm, and Victor joined his company. Armand soon bought out the other partner, who had been ruined in the stock market collapse, and the Hammer Galleries were established. Meanwhile the Hammer palace in Moscow rivalled any museum of decorative arts, and their acquisitions also filled several warehouses. Having paid a tax to the Soviets, they were allowed to export these treasures, and this became the stock which Armand and Victor brilliantly sold in the Hammer Galleries over a period of years. This, the first Hammer Collection, has all been dispersed. It was essentially a way of converting rubles into dollars.

Thus for a long time art dealing has been the avocation of Armand Hammer. He is the President of the Hammer Galleries although Victor is the active manager. But Armand's real vocation has been a search for still more rewarding enterprises. In Russia, apart from his export-import business, he built and operated a pencil factory which at its peak produced seventy-two million pencils and ninety-five million pens a year and made a tremendous profit. Departing from Russia in 1930, he ran a private bank in Paris, which specialized in discounting Soviet notes at twenty-four per cent per annum, holding them until they were paid in full, and often making as much as seventy per cent on each transaction. He then returned to America, and after having sold most of his Russian collection, helped liquidate the Hearst works of art.

During World War II he built the first distillery in this country to make alcohol from potatoes; and substituting potato spirits for grain spirits, which were embargoed, he developed a valuable business in blended whiskey. After the war he bought several other distilleries which used the more conventional grain alcohol. In a few years he built the J. W. Dant brand from a relatively unknown Kentucky bourbon into a company selling over a million cases a year. In 1954 he finally sold this whiskey empire to Schenley Distillers and moved to California. But his most successful venture was his investment in Occidental Petroleum, of which he has been President and is now Chairman. To give some idea of the growth of this company under his leadership, in 1956, when he first became associated with it, its total assets were under forty thousand dollars; today they are two and one-half billion dollars.

Occidental Petroleum has made possible the third Hammer Collection. For there was a second Hammer Collection formed in the fifties and given to the

University of Southern California in 1965. These paintings comprise an important group of Old Masters intended for study purposes and have proved invaluable in a university museum. But when he had given them away, Dr. Hammer began a more ambitious collection with a particular emphasis on French Impressionists, Post-Impressionists, and Old Master paintings and drawings. This, the third Hammer Collection, is illustrated and annotated in the present catalog.

Though the focus is on paintings of the nineteenth and twentieth centuries, the work of earlier masters is represented. The Los Angeles County Museum of Art was enabled by the Armand and Frances Hammer Purchase Fund to acquire two splendid seventeenth-century panels: Rembrandt's *Portrait of a Man of the Raman Family* and Rubens' *The Israelites Gathering Manna in the Desert*. A second Rubens in the Hammer Collection, *Young Woman with Curly Hair*, is particularly distinguished for its flesh tones, as beautiful as any I know in painting, and for its modeling, breathtaking in the subtlety of the transitions of shadow.

There are only two eighteenth-century paintings in the exhibition. The first, Fragonard's *The Education of the Virgin*, owes its chiaroscuro and sepia tones to Rembrandt and its fluent brushwork and virtuosity to Rubens. The second, a sketch by Goya, *El Pelele*, for the Prado cartoon, was selected by the Spanish Society of the Friends of Art for their exhibition of Goya's work in Madrid, a fact worth noting, since only the finest Spanish pictures meet their exacting standards.

Corot has always been for Armand Hammer a favorite artist. At one time there were twenty-four of his paintings in the collection. Of these only the seven finest are being shown. Historically the most interesting is a landscape known as *Pleasures of Evening*, an appropriate title for it is one of the artist's

last canvases. Writing about it in 1892, Castagnary touchingly said, "When the imagination is still so fresh, and sensitivity still so alive, death should take pity and not interrupt." The painting has darkened with time, as happens often with Corot's late work. Thus there will always be those who prefer the fresh, spring-like tones of *Distant View of Mantes Cathedral*. For my part I would choose the dramatic *Medieval Ruins*, or, among figure pictures, the portrait of a young minx whose half-smile and appraising glance enthrall me.

With Corot as its leader, the greatest school of landscape painting the world has known, even without the geniuses of Constable and Turner, flourished in and around Paris. To realize this one need only look at Boudin, whose mastery of cloud effects is impressively demonstrated by *Sailing Ships in Port*; at Renoir, whose infectious *joie de vivre* is gloriously apparent both in *Grape Pickers at Lunch*, an enchanting peasant picnic, and in *Antibes*, which suggests a modern *Embarkation for Cythera*; and at Monet whose palette, in that masterpiece of light and air, *View of Bordighera*, seems made of ground jewels. All these paintings illustrate the reason for the popularity of the Impressionists and their circle.

One of the most enchanting cityscapes ever painted, Pissarro's *Boulevard Montmartre, Mardi Gras*, which recently moved from one California collector to another, from Norton Simon to Armand Hammer, shows the quintessence of this Impressionist technique. It vibrates with light and color, an effect only possible through the use of those quick, short brush strokes which are the hallmark of Impressionism.

There was, of course, the reaction against the Impressionists, exemplified by Cézanne, van Gogh, and Gauguin. All these artists are well represented in the Hammer Collection. The Cézanne *Boy Resting* has been frequently exhibited; the Gauguin *Bonjour M.*

Gauguin, a later version of which is in Prague, has been widely reproduced; and the four van Goghs, *Garden of the Rectory at Nuenen,* an early work, *The Sower,* somewhat later and obviously influenced by Millet, *Lilacs,* a still life seemingly redolent of the fragrance of lilacs, and *Hospital at St. Rémy,* where van Gogh was confined, are all well known. The latter, once in the Norton Simon Collection, is one of van Gogh's supreme works. Of this view of the park and the asylum he wrote, "I tried to reconstruct the thing as it might have been, simplifying and accentuating the haughty, unchanging character of the pines and cedar clumps against the blue." There are also superb drawings by these three artists, which include eighteen sketches by Gauguin, five by van Gogh, and four by Cézanne.

American collectors have been so preoccupied with the Impressionists and their followers that there has been a tendency to overlook artists who did not belong to the movement. Among these to me the most enthralling is Gustave Moreau, who was a direct precursor of the Surrealists. Armand Hammer owns two of his masterpieces, *King David* and *Salome.* The latter had a deep effect on J. K. Huysman, and in *A Rebours* he wrote a long description of the picture in prose as glittering as the painting itself. In 1876 P. de Saint-Victor said of it: "M. Gustave Moreau's entry in the Salon far excels any of his previous exhibits. . . . If an opium fiend could translate his visions into reality with a goldsmith's skill, it would give some idea of this artist."

Another French artist less collected than he deserves to be is Fantin-Latour. His still lifes of flowers are often to be found in American collections, though never in a finer example than Dr. Hammer's *Peonies in a Blue and White Vase,* but his superb portraits are too rarely seen. *Portrait of Miss Edith Crowe* is one of the most poetic examples of nineteenth-century portraiture. The strongly accented light and shadow create a mood of pensive brooding, the essence of the Romantic image.

The momentum of the great French artistic movements of the nineteenth century carried creativity well into the first half of the twentieth century. The artists who made Paris in our time the mecca for painters, especially Vuillard and Bonnard, are beautifully shown. It is difficult to choose among the Vuillards, they are all of such high quality. But my favorite remains *At the Seashore.* Jacques Salomon in a recent book perfectly expresses my response to this exquisite canvas when he says it "is like a cry from the heart, the echo of which ravished me. . . the touch is so alive, so alert, so completely submissive to the rhythm of Vuillard's feeling."

Bonnard, too, is well represented. The early *Street Scene* evokes the loveliness of the simplest happenings of Parisian life, and the *Nude against the Light* suggests the artist's unique combination of sensitivity and sensuality, reminding one of the nudes Titian painted at the end of his life.

Different from the serene beauty of Vuillard and Bonnard but of considerable historical importance is van Dongen's *Friends.* Painted between 1908 and 1909 this canvas foretells German Expressionism in subject and handling and proves once more that until World War II Paris was the center of all new movements in art.

The next generation which lends such lustre to the School of Paris is to be seen in a great portrait by Modigliani, already a part of the collection of the Los Angeles County Museum of Art; by Vlaminck's *Summer Bouquet,* equaling de Staël in its display of palette knife virtuosity; and by Derain's *Still Life with Basket, Jug and Fruit* which is distinguished for its simplicity of composition, its elimination to essential forms, and its restricted palette.

I have kept to the last two paintings, both as insubstantial as a dream: Marie Laurencin's *Women in the Forest*, which once belonged to John Quinn, the pioneer among American collectors in his appreciation of the School of Paris; and Chagall's *Blue Angel*, which was once in the collection of Frank Crowninshield, the able editor of *Vanity Fair*, a publication largely responsible for the American vogue of these Parisian artists.

In recent years Dr. Hammer has added to his collection a few American paintings. His earliest picture is the most famous of American icons, Gilbert Stuart's *Portrait of George Washington*. Known as the "Lewis Washington," it is more interesting than many other versions, showing the first President seated at a table with his sword resting on his arm and a glimpse of sky in the distance.

A great portrait painted just eighty years later is Thomas Eakins' *Sebastiano Cardinal Martinelli*. In its psychological penetration, its simplicity and dignity, its noble humanity, this may well be considered an American Rembrandt. Sylvan Schendler, writing in 1967, refers to it as "the most powerful portrait of its kind ever painted by an American."

Slightly earlier is a fine still life by Harnett, which has the distinction of being among the few nineteenth-century American pictures ever exhibited at the Royal Academy, where it was shown in 1885 and bought by an English painter, George Richmond.

The latest in date of the American canvases is *On the Beach*, painted in 1916 by Maurice Prendergast, the most original and interesting of American Impressionists. Owned by Mrs. Charles Prendergast until recently, it is a picture she parted with reluctantly as it was always considered in the family one of her brother-in-law's greatest masterpieces.

Two Americans who lived abroad, Mary Cassatt and John Singer Sargent, are superbly represented, each by two pictures, one of the Sargents having been bought by the Los Angeles County Museum of Art with funds provided by Dr. and Mrs. Hammer. Mary Cassatt's double portrait of Reine Lefebvre and Margot is in my opinion her finest pastel done after 1900, and the idyllic *Summertime* I consider one of her two most important landscapes.

The two portraits by Sargent, though both were painted relatively early, are totally different from each other. *Dr. Pozzi at Home*, dated 1881, is highly dramatic, as though the doctor were an actor about to go on stage. It is a masterpiece of Salon painting, sophisticated and cosmopolitan. The double portrait of Mrs. Edward L. Davis and her son, Livingston Davis, is much more sober, more American in a straight-forward, realistic way. Sargent has here recorded the essence of upper class America, which has learned to be fashionable without learning to be chic.

I have already mentioned a few of the drawings owned by Dr. Hammer. In recent years this part of his collection has been greatly enriched, and his finest acquisitions have been made in 1970 and 1971. These begin with a lovely watercolor of flowers by Albrecht Dürer, a study by Raphael for S. Maria della Pace in Rome, and two studies by Correggio, one for the pendentive of San Giovanni Evangelista in Parma and the other for the Madonna della Scodella, both published in 1970 by Oberhuber. Another discovery is a biblical subject by Rembrandt in the process of being published by Christopher White.

Dr. Hammer's interest in drawings increases, however, when we reach the eighteenth and nineteenth centuries. At the sale of Mrs. Jesse I. Straus's fastidiously chosen collection he bought two exquisite sanguines by Watteau, four virtuoso performances in sepia wash by Fragonard, a serenely beautiful pencil portrait of Mrs. Badham drawn by Ingres when he was in Rome, and the fascinating Degas pastel of M. Jacquet, whose staring eyes are so strangely hypnotic.

From the Norton Simon sale he acquired two Boucher drawings, one *Venus Reclining Against a Dolphin*, which was engraved by Demarteau, and the other, *Landscape*, which was selected by Agnes Mongan for *Great Drawings of All Times*. He also bid in at the same sale a superb nineteenth-century watercolor: *Peasants Resting* by Millet and a drawing, *The Model Full-Face*, related to the large oil *The Models* (1887) in the Barnes Foundation, by Seurat. At the Hugh Chisholm Sale he bought a black chalk drawing by Manet of a beautiful young man, who looks down disdainfully at the spectator. One can imagine this superb sketch as a symbol of that protective contempt assumed by the Impressionists after their public rejection.

The Hammer Collection contains only one work by Daumier, a drawing in watercolor, ink, and gouache, of a lawyer pleading for his client, but it ranks among the artist's finest achievements. The old bespectacled advocate is vibrant with passion, and the whole court seems caught up in the intensity of the drama. One is almost overwhelmed by the concentrated endeavor of the unknown lawyer.

Talking to Armand Hammer one feels something of the same intellectual concentration. To any problem confronting him a solution must be found, whether in his youth it involved the pharmaceutical company or Russian famine, or later the sale of Fordson tractors or the manufacture of lead pencils, or after his Russian sojourn the dispersal of his first art collection or the distilling of whiskey, or today the development of the Occidental Petroleum Company, or the search for a cure for cancer through the Armand Hammer Center for Cancer Research at the Salk Institute in La Jolla, California. Not the least of his endeavors is the assembling of the present collection of works of art for the benefit of the public.

Armand Hammer is not like other collectors. His delight is in the quest, not the possession. None of his great paintings or drawings hang in his house. He is satisfied to live with a fine copy by Mrs. Hammer of the Modigliani portrait bought with his funds by the Los Angeles County Museum of Art, and with a few Impressionist paintings of slight importance. At seventy-three he works as hard as anyone I have ever known. Much of his life is spent in his airplane flying from one place to another, tirelessly seeking to improve the earnings of Occidental Petroleum. He feels a deep sense of obligation to the shareholders, but he is also interested in making more money himself. Why? For the sheer joy of giving it away. It may or may not be true that it is more blessed to give than to receive. But Armand Hammer would say it is certainly much more fun!

John Walker

Director Emeritus, National Gallery of Art, Washington, D.C.

Foreword

Ever since the days of Giorgio Vasari, drawings have exerted an immense appeal to collectors. Many reasons explain why this should have been so; for one thing, drawings do not take up much space, and, for another, they often provide some insight into the workings of an artist's mind.

Dr. Armand Hammer started to collect drawings relatively recently, but this has not prevented him from acquiring a number of first-class items. As several of these are little known, this exhibition will provide the art historian with an opportunity to familiarize himself with fresh material. A particularly fascinating early drawing, for instance, which was first exhibited as recently as 1969, is the double-sided sheet by Correggio. The recto of this drawing consists of a sketch for the pendentive with Sts. Matthew and Jerome in San Giovanni Evangelista at Parma, and this happy combination of red chalk and pen produced that mood of mystery which is one of this master's chief attributes. The verso, in the same medium, is a sketch for the *Madonna della Scodella* and has a spirited touch that announces the baroque.

Nowadays few collectors can secure a drawing by Raphael, a master whose relevance in terms of modern sentiment has recently been made clear by Sir John Pope-Hennessy. Dr. Hammer has been fortunate enough to acquire a splendid, if unfamiliar, drawing by this artist. This masterly drawing represents the Prophet Hosea and Jonah with an angel and is a study for the fresco in S. Maria della Pace, Rome, and, a feature always attractive to the collector of drawings, it enjoys a distinguished provenance for it once belonged to Jonathan Richardson, Mariette, and Richard Payne-Knight. Another unexpected item in the collection is a watercolor of flowers by Dürer. This is one of those lyrical drawings of flowers which emphasizes the curiosity shown by this sixteenth-century Humanist into all types of phenomena.

One of the most attractive features of the draftsman's art is the way in which the artist of genius can suggest the essence of a theme with economy and understanding. Such concision and feeling for the dramatic moment are apparent in Rembrandt's *A Biblical Subject*, a drawing which was unknown until its rare appearance at auction in 1971. The style of this effective drawing may be related to that of *Isaac and Rebecca Spied upon by Amelach*, in the S. Kramarsky Collection, New York, and it probably dates from the 1660s, the last decade of the artist's life.

G. B. Tiepolo, that magical master of the eighteenth-century Venetian School, is often considered solely as an evoker of the pleasures of life, and consequently it is sometimes overlooked that he had a profound religious sense. The lightness of touch in the technique of *The Virgin and Child with Saints*, a celebrated drawing from the Orloff Collection, does not diminish the religious feeling, evident in the haggard figure over whom the Virgin stretches a protective arm. The same emotional intensity is discernible in the figure of St. Jerome in the bold drawing, *St. Jerome in the Desert Listening to the Angels*; it is an intensity similar to that found in much contemporary religious sculpture.

One of the strengths of the collection is the representation of the eighteenth-century French School. Two of the most intriguing and enchanting drawings in it are by Antoine Watteau, one of the most elegant and sensitive of draftsmen. *Young Girl* is a sheet which old hands will recall from its appearance in the famous exhibition of French art at the Royal Academy in 1932. It is a casual study sketched in red and black chalks and suggests the extent to which Watteau, a northerner, was in debt to the Dutch tradition. The artist has been able to endow this reticent drawing with a touch of the melancholy which haunted his own personality and permitted him to evoke the transient element in life.

Watteau was in love with drawing. He filled sketchbooks with his studies, many of which were used for his paintings. A case in point is the study of a man and a girl seated on the ground which, once again, is a delicious combination of red and black chalks; it was used for two of Watteau's paintings, *La Famille* and *L'Assemblée Galante*. It is a drawing which has the master's special qualities—beautiful hands that quiver as if they were those of some great pianist about to perform a prelude by Chopin, and sharply accented features that reveal the intelligence so characteristic of his figures.

Honoré Fragonard is admirably represented in the collection. He has been principally admired as the painter of pretty and vivacious women and as a master of brio. As did Franz Hals, he gloried in the properties of paint, enjoying the ripples made by pigment on a canvas and creating a proto-romantic image of his sitters. There is often something a touch theatrical in his paintings. What has not been sufficiently emphasized is the way in which he could take a conventional genre subject and give it a magical quality. It is only necessary to look at *Grandfather's Reprimand* to see how he could treat the sort of theme which appealed to the anecdotic school of the nineteenth century and yet present it with an artistic twist. Each actor in the story is individualized, and the play of grey-brown wash over the black chalk creates a warm chiaroscuro effect. Splendid passages occur in this drawing such as the still life with the open book which harks back to the world of Rembrandt and, in so doing, substantiates the truth of Focillon's concept of the *famille d' esprit*.

Fragonard's subject matter is interesting. In the *Visit to the Nurse* the theme is apparently taken from the novel *Sarah TH,* which was translated from the English in 1765 by Saint-Lambert, a friend of Grimm and Mlle. d'Houdetot. It points to Fragonard's connection with the milieu of Diderot and the Encyclopaedists, and, as Diderot's writings prove, a love of eroticism and instruction is not incompatible. The two other drawings by Fragonard are *The Little Preacher* and *The Reading.*

The exhibition of Boucher's paintings held at the Louvre in 1971 suggested that, like Fragonard, this master stands in need of revaluation: this show stressed his qualities as a painter of flesh and of magical color; it also brought out his skill and individuality as a landscapist. Two drawings in the collection show him in both aspects. *Venus Reclining Against a Dolphin* is one of the characteristic tributes which Boucher, master of the Rococo, paid to Venus; the girl has beautiful features and an ample form, and the drawing has that special quality which this artist could often command: the illusion that the figure is floating in space. In this drawing, too, piquancy is supplied by the dolphin which has the touch of the proverbial satyr. The other drawing is a landscape which reveals that Boucher, like Bonnard, was able to transform a simple rustic scene into the setting for a *fête galante,* and the pencil strokes are endowed with a silken touch.

This collection suggests the tradition of French draftsmanship from the eighteenth century onward, one that is rich in contrasts, as between, for instance, Ingres' polished *Mrs. Badham* and Daumier's *The Pleading Lawyer.* Ingres' sitter, the first cousin of the poet Thomas Campbell, is a true beauty of the *Keepsake* variety with a touch of simper about her; she symbolizes a world of comfort and privilege. Daumier, on the other hand, takes us into the battle of the courts —the lawyer pleads with a dramatic eloquence which is not without a hint of cynicism.

Continuity is ever-present in French draftsmanship.

The note of melancholy which marks the art of Watteau recurs in a drawing such as Degas' *Jacquet.* This note may also be observed in Seurat's simple and elegant study of a nude after *The Models* of 1886-1888 in the Barnes Collection.

One of the finest nineteenth-century drawings in the collection is J. F. Millet's pastel *Peasants Resting.* There was a time when this master was one of the most sought-after painters of the day for whose work high prices were paid. Then he fell out of fashion; he was considered too anecdotic and moralistic for modern taste. Now, rightly, the conception of Millet has changed. He is beginning to be appreciated as a master whose delicate sense of tone and feeling for form relate him to the early Italians. This pastel is executed with considerable subtlety; the relationship of the two blocked-in figures to the tree on the left and the gently indicated middle and far distance is admirably achieved. It is understandable that Millet appealed so deeply to van Gogh. It is a relationship excellently illustrated in this collection by the two charcoal landscape drawings, *The Zandmennik House* and *The Margrot House, Cuesmes,* in which the absence of human beings and the sparse treatment of the subject conjure up a magical and almost surrealistic atmosphere. The Dutch artist's search for form is revealed, too, in the strong studies of a *Man Polishing a Boot* and an *Old Man Carrying a Bucket.* The individuality of van Gogh's early period is emphasized as well by the atmospheric watercolor, *The Weaver.*

The range of French draftsmanship in the nineteenth century becomes clear from this collection. One of the most powerful drawings is Toulouse-Lautrec's *Dance at the Moulin de la Galette,* which is particularly interesting, for it was made by the artist after the famous painting of the same subject, now in the Art Institute of Chicago, for publication in the *Courrier*

Français of May 19, 1889. It is one of those drawings which brings out the relationship between his approach and technique and those of Raffaëlli, another connoisseur of the Parisian scene.

It is only relatively recently that Manet's style as a draftsman has received detailed attention. The *Study of a Man Wearing a Cloak* is a remarkable sheet—bold in execution, disdainful in pose. It is hard not to feel that this is a drawing which would have appealed to Baudelaire. Another intriguing drawing is Cézanne's *Study of the "Ecorché"* which has affinities with Tintoretto; the verso is valuable for it contains a study for the portrait of the artist's father, given by Paul Mellon to the National Gallery of Art. Bonnard, Boudin, Monet, Pissarro, Picasso, and Renoir are other nineteenth- and twentieth-century artists represented in the collection by important drawings.

Special mention must also be made of the group of drawings by Paul Gauguin. These include the highly important *Sketchbook* which the artist bought in Rouen in 1884 and used intermittently in Denmark and Brittany between 1884 and 1888. The vivid pencil and chalk sketches of Breton peasants — the lads are singularly charming, all their shyness captured—and the Breton landscape provided material which the artist used for pictures of the same period. The sketchbook also contains Gauguin's *Notes Synthétiques:* the first occasion, as far as is known, on which he adumbrated his aesthetic theories.

The collection also includes one of this master's most enigmatic Breton pictures — the famous *Bonjour M. Gauguin,* which was inspired by Courbet and painted in the autumn of 1889 to decorate the dining room of Marie Henry's inn at Le Pouldu. It seems as if this painting precedes the other version in the National Gallery, Prague.

Corot is clearly one of Dr. Hammer's favorite painters, and the collector has shown his independence of judgment in admiring the late, as well as the early style, of this master. It has become fashionable to denigrate Corot's later poetical canvases, but the moods they evoke — dreamy and wistful — are persuasive in their impact. Indeed, a masterpiece of the final period such as *Pleasures of Evening,* which was exhibited in the Salon of 1875, the year of the artist's death, shows how a Claudian vision of nature survived in nineteenth-century France. In the case of the exquisitely judged *View of Mantes,* which was painted a decade or so earlier, the evocative mood is akin to that found in the pictures of Watteau and Bonnard.

The painters of the French School of the nineteenth century, like the masters of Dutch painting during the Golden Age, had a wonderful eye for tone. This is apparent in the two superb flowerpieces by Fantin-Latour in the collection, and it gives the *Portrait of Miss Edith Crowe* its restrained distinction. It is this feeling for the proper blending of color that also endows Degas' *Three Dancers in Yellow Skirts* with rich vibrancy and, in his case, makes him a precursor of the emotive and dramatic color of Fauvism.

Like many contemporary collectors, Dr. Hammer has acquired representative pictures by the Impressionists such as Pissarro's sparkling *Boulevard Montmartre, Mardi Gras,* Monet's sun-drenched *View of Bordighera,* and Renoir's *Grape Pickers at Lunch.* These are pictures that bring out the *joie de vivre* which is one of the principal contributions of this School. The Impressionists are painters who celebrate the delights of nature. Their works now have another claim on our attention. Thirty or so years ago the Impressionist townscape or landscape gave a more or less true picture of the world that lay around us, but now, after so much devastation, they have a nostalgic quality; they recall a golden land.

The collection also contains a number of important examples of Post-Impressionism: Cézanne, Gauguin, Toulouse-Lautrec, and van Gogh. One of the most fascinating paintings, for instance, is Toulouse-Lautrec's *In the Salon,* which shows Rolande and a friend and is a study for the *Salon de la rue des Moulins* in the Museum at Albi. It is a picture in which the artist employs a dramatic color, red, to emphasize the character of the scene. One of the major pictures is van Gogh's famous *Hospital at Saint-Rémy* in which the tormented pines and cedars have a magnetic attraction.

Toulouse-Lautrec and van Gogh painted a world which was very different from that favored by Vuillard and Bonnard. Vuillard is an artist whose appeal never diminishes, for he had the rare gift of suggesting the privacy of sensation. His small pictures of interiors or his views of Parisian scenes show the delight that the subtle eye may derive from the contemplation of color values and unusual angles of vision.

Dr. Hammer admires those nineteenth-century artists who are only now being admired as they deserve, such as Gustave Moreau and J. S. Sargent; he has acquired important pictures by both masters. Moreau is an artist who expressed the rich and eclectic culture of the *fin de siècle,* and his dramatic *Salome* has the spicy flavor of Richard Strauss's famous opera. Sargent's *Dr. Pozzi at Home* demonstrates the brilliance of this master's technique as well as his debt to Carolus-Duran. The histrionic air of this marvelous portrait makes a comparison inevitable with Whistler's celebrated portrait of *Sir Henry Irving* in The Metropolitan Museum of Art. The American School is well shown in the collection with two first-class paintings by Mary Cassatt, the *Portrait of George Washington* which Gilbert Stuart painted for Lewis in 1822, the *Still Life* by William Harnett, which was exhibited at the Royal Academy in 1885, Thomas Eakins' searching *Portrait of Sebastiano Cardinal Martinelli,* a masterpiece of realism, and *On the Beach* by Maurice Prendergast.

The emphasis on the nineteenth century in this collection does not mean that Old Masters have been excluded. There is a fine Rembrandt, *Portrait of a Man of the Raman Family,* in which the white ruff is an exercise in bravura painting and two splendid works by Rubens. One is the brilliant sketch of a young girl with curly hair, and the other an important *modello, The Israelites Gathering Manna in the Desert,* for the *Triumph of the Eucharist* series in which the artist's fertile invention and powerful sense of color are displayed. Sketches, like drawings, attract Dr. Hammer, and the section devoted to Old Masters in the collection includes Fragonard's *The Education of the Virgin* and Goya's *El Pelele,* which was executed in connection with a series of designs for tapestries dealing with popular Spanish life.

The collection is rounded off with a number of twentieth-century paintings. These include a monumental portrait of a woman by Modigliani, a saucy picture, *Friends,* by Kees van Dongen, a whimsical composition by Marie Laurencin, and an austere still life by Derain. Collections of this eclectic type are relatively rare in our period, and the scope of this one will afford the visitor a number of unusual pleasures.

Denys Sutton

Editor of APOLLO

European Paintings

I   Rembrandt van Rijn (1606-1669)
     Portrait of a Man of the Raman Family
     Oil on oval panel
     25½″ x 19⅞″ (64.8 x 50.5 cm.)

2   Peter Paul Rubens (1577-1640)
     Young Woman with Curly Hair
     Oil on panel
     26⅜″ x 20½″ (67.0 x 52.1 cm.)

3   Peter Paul Rubens (1577-1640)
     *The Israelites Gathering Manna
     in the Desert*
     Oil on panel
     25½″ x 20¾″ (64.8 x 52.7 cm.)

4   Jean-Honoré Fragonard (1732-1806)
The Education of the Virgin
Oil on panel
11 13/16″ x 9⅝″ (30.3 x 24.4 cm.)

5   Francisco Goya (1746-1828)
        El Pelele
        Oil on canvas
        14″ x 9⅛″ (35.6 x 23.2 cm.)

6   Théodore Géricault (1791-1824)
     Portrait of a Gentleman
     Oil on canvas
     25⅝″ x 21¼″ (65.1 x 54.0 cm.)

7   Camille Corot (1796-1875)
     Portrait of a Girl
     Oil on canvas
     12¼″ x 9³/₁₆″ (32.1 x 24.3 cm.)

8   Camille Corot (1796-1875)
Medieval Ruins
Oil on canvas, mounted on board
9″ x 12″ (23.0 x 30.5 cm.)

9   Camille Corot (1796-1875)
     Harvester Under Trees
     Oil on canvas
     15 ¹³⁄₁₆″ x 12″ (40.1 x 30.5 cm.)

10   Camille Corot (1796-1875)
     Distant View of Mantes Cathedral
     Oil on canvas
     22 $\frac{1}{16}$″ x 18 $\frac{1}{16}$″ (56.0 x 45.9 cm.)

11   Camille Corot (1796-1875)
Grape Harvest at Sèvres
Oil on canvas
16⅞″ x 29⅜″ (42.8 x 74.6 cm.)

12   Camille Corot (1796-1875)
      Morning
      Oil on canvas
      69 11/16″ x 52⅜″ (177.0 x 133.0 cm.)

13   Camille Corot (1796-1875)
      Pleasures of Evening
      Oil on canvas
      44½″ x 65³⁄₁₆″ (113.0 x 165.6 cm.)

14   Eugène Boudin (1824-1898)
      Sailing Ships in Port
      Oil on canvas
      17¾" x 25⁵⁄₁₆" (45.1 x 64.3 cm.)

15 Eugène Boudin (1824-1898)
    Quay at Camaret
    Oil on canvas
    14½″ x 23″ (36.8 x 58.4 cm.)

16   Eugène Boudin (1824-1898)
      Beach at Trouville
      Oil on canvas
      12⅞″ x 7⁵⁄₁₆″ (32.7 x 18.6 cm.)

17 Gustave Caillebotte (1848-1894)
    Square in Argenteuil
    Oil on canvas
    23 13/16'' x 27¾'' (60.5 x 70.5 cm.)

18 Alfred Sisley (1839-1899)
    Timber Yard at Saint-Mammès
    Oil on canvas
    21½″ x 28¾″ (55.6 x 72.9 cm.)

19 Claude Monet (1840-1926)
    View of Bordighera
    Oil on canvas
    26″ x 32¼″ (66.0 x 81.9 cm.)

20   Pierre Auguste Renoir (1841-1919)
      Two Girls Reading
      Oil on canvas
      22″ x 18⅝″ (55.9 x 47.2 cm.)

21 Pierre Auguste Renoir (1841-1919)
Antibes
Oil on canvas
25½″ x 32″ (64.8 x 81.3 cm.)

22   Pierre Auguste Renoir (1841-1919)
      Grape Pickers at Lunch
      Oil on canvas
      21⅞″ x 18¼″ (55.5 x 46.4 cm.)

23   Camille Pissarro (1830-1903)
      Boulevard Montmartre, Mardi Gras
      Oil on canvas
      25″ x 31½″ (63.5 x 77.5 cm.)

24 Henri Fantin-Latour (1836-1904)
    Peonies in a Blue and White Vase
    Oil on canvas
    23$\frac{15}{16}$'' x 19$\frac{5}{8}$'' (60.8 x 49.9 cm.)

25 Henri Fantin-Latour (1836-1904)
Portrait of Miss Edith Crowe
Oil on canvas
28¾″ x 23⁵⁄₁₆″ (73.0 x 59.2 cm.)

26 Henri Fantin-Latour (1836-1904)
   Roses
   Oil on canvas
   26¹⁄₁₆″ x 22¹¹⁄₁₆″ (66.2 x 57.7 cm.)

27 Edgar Degas (1834-1917)
Three Dancers in Yellow Skirts
Oil on canvas
32″ x 25⅝″ (81.3 x 65.1 cm.)

28   Gustave Moreau (1826-1898)
      King David
      Oil on canvas
      90⁹⁄₁₆″ x 54⁵⁄₁₆″ (230.0 x 137.6 cm.)

29　Gustave Moreau (1826-1898)
　　Salome
　　Oil on canvas
　　56⅝″ x 41 1/16″ (143.8 x 104.2 cm.)

30 Paul Cézanne (1839-1906)
    Boy Resting
    Oil on canvas
    21⁷⁄₁₆″ x 25¹³⁄₁₆″ (54.5 x 65.5 cm.)

31 Henri de Toulouse-Lautrec (1864-1901)
    In the Salon
    Oil on cardboard
    15¾″ x 23⅞″ (40.0 x 60.6 cm.)

32   Emile Bernard (1868-1941)
      Wheat Harvest
      Oil on canvas
      28½″ x 35⅞″ (72.4 x 91.1 cm.)

33 Paul Gauguin (1848-1903)
Bonjour M. Gauguin
Oil on canvas, mounted on panel
29½″ x 21½″ (74.9 x 54.6 cm.)

34　Vincent van Gogh (1853-1890)
Garden of the Rectory at Nuenen
Oil on canvas, mounted on panel
20⅞″ x 30¾″ (53.0 x 78.2 cm.)

35   Vincent van Gogh (1853-1890)
     Lilacs
     Oil on canvas
     10¾″ x 13¹⁵/₁₆″ (27.3 x 35.3 cm.)

36　Vincent van Gogh (1853-1890)
The Sower
Oil on canvas
13¼″ x 15¹⁵⁄₁₆″ (33.6 x 40.4 cm.)

37   Vincent van Gogh (1853-1890)
Hospital at Saint-Rémy
Oil on canvas
35½″ x 28″ (90.2 x 71.1 cm.)

38   Pierre Bonnard (1867-1947)
      Street Scene
      Oil on canvas
      21″ x 27½″ (53.3 x 69.8 cm.)

39   Pierre Bonnard (1867-1947)
      Nude against the Light
      Oil on canvas
      48¾″ x 21½″ (123.8 x 54.6 cm.)

40   Edouard Vuillard (1868-1940)
     In the Bus
     Oil on board
     9¹³⁄₁₆″ x 9″ (25.0 x 22.9 cm.)

41 Edouard Vuillard (1868-1940)
Rue Lepic, Paris
Tempera
65″ x 18½″ (165.1 x 47.0 cm.)

42 Edouard Vuillard (1868-1940)
    At the Seashore
    Oil on panel
    8½″ x 8½″ (21.6 x 21.6 cm.)

43   Edouard Vuillard (1868-1940)
Interior
Oil on board
21⅛″ x 15⅞″ (53.3 x 40.3 cm.)

44 André Derain (1880-1954)
Still Life with Basket, Jug and Fruit
Oil on canvas
19⅞″ x 23¹¹/₁₆″ (50.5 x 60.1 cm.)

45 Amedeo Modigliani (1884-1920)
Woman of the People
Oil on canvas
39¼″ x 25⅜″ (99.7 x 65.1 cm.)

46 Maurice de Vlaminck (1876-1958)
    Summer Bouquet
    Oil on canvas
    25¾″ x 21⁹⁄₁₆″ (65.4 x 54.7 cm.)

47 Georges Rouault (1871-1958)
Circus Girl
Oil on paper
25¾″ x 20¹¹/₁₆″ (65.4 x 52.5 cm.)

48   Kees van Dongen (1877-1968)
Friends
Oil on canvas
39⅜″ x 31⅞″ (100.0 x 80.9 cm.)

49 Marie Laurencin (1885-1956)
Women in the Forest
Oil on canvas
31⅞″ x 39⅝″ (81.0 x 107.0 cm.)

50   Marc Chagall (1887-   )
      Blue Angel
      Gouache and pastel
      20″ x 26″ (50.8 x 66.1 cm.)

American Paintings

51　Gilbert Stuart (1755-1828)
Portrait of George Washington
Oil on canvas
44⅛" x 34½" (112.0 x 87.6 cm.)

52 William Michael Harnett (1848-1892)
    Still Life
    Oil on panel
    13¾ʺ x 10⁵⁄₁₆ʺ (34.9 x 26.2 cm.)

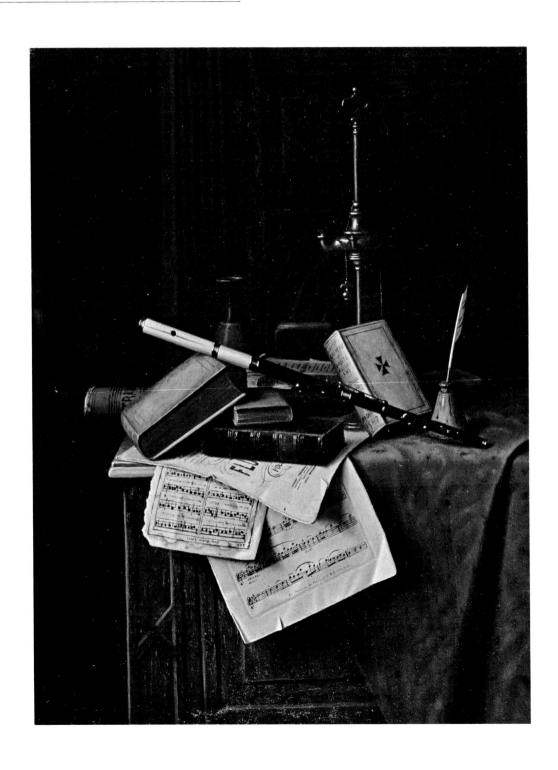

53   John Singer Sargent (1856-1925)
     Dr. Pozzi at Home
     Oil on canvas
     80½″ x 43⅞″ (204.5 x 111.5 cm.)

54   John Singer Sargent (1856-1925)
      Portrait of Mrs. Edward L. Davis and Her
      Son, Livingston Davis
      Oil on canvas
      86″ x 48″ (218.4 x 121.9 cm.)

55 Thomas Eakins (1844-1916)
Portrait of Sebastiano Cardinal Martinelli
Oil on canvas, mounted on panel
78⁵/₁₆″ x 59¹⁵/₁₆″ (198.9 x 152.3 cm.)

56 Mary Cassatt (1844-1926)
    Reine Lefebvre and Margot
    Pastel on brown paper, mounted on canvas
    32¾″ x 26⁹/₁₆″ (83.2 x 67.5 cm.)

57   Mary Cassatt (1844-1926)
      Summertime
      Oil on canvas
      28⅞″ x 39⅜″ (73.4 x 100.0 cm.)

58   Maurice Brazil Prendergast (1861-1924)
      On the Beach
      Oil on canvas
      26¾" x 39" (67.9 x 99.0 cm.)

59   Andrew Wyeth (1917-   )
       Brandywine Valley
       Watercolor
       21″ x 29″ (53.3 x 73.7 cm.)

Drawings & Watercolors

60 Albrecht Dürer (1471-1528)
Tuft of Cowslips
Gouache on vellum
7⁹⁄₁₆'' x 6⅝'' (19.2 x 16.8 cm.)

61 Raphael Sanzio (1483-1520)
Study for a Fresco with Hosea and Jonah
Pen and brown wash, heightened with white
10⅝" x 7¹³⁄₁₆" (26.2 x 19.8 cm.)

62   Antonio Allegri da Correggio (1494-1534)
      Pendentive Study with Sts. Matthew
      and Jerome (recto)
      Ink and red chalk
      8¼″ x 5½″ (21.0 x 14.0 cm.)

Study for the "Madonna della Scodella"
(verso)
Ink and red chalk
7¹⁵⁄₁₆″ x 5″ (20.2 x 12.7 cm.)

63 Rembrandt van Rijn (1606-1669)
    A Biblical Subject
    Pen and ink, brown wash, heightened with
    white
    6¹³/₁₆″ x 6¾″ (17.3 x 17.2 cm.)

64 Jean Antoine Watteau (1684-1721)
Young Girl
Red and black chalk
8½″ x 5¾″ (21.6 x 14.6 cm.)

65 Jean Antoine Watteau (1684-1721)
Couple Seated on a Bank
Red, black, and white chalk on buff paper
9½″ x 13¾″ (24.1 x 34.9 cm.)

66 Giovanni Battista Tiepolo (1696-1770)
Virgin and Child Adored by Bishops,
Monks, and Women
Pen and bister wash over black chalk on
white paper
16¾" x 11¹³⁄₁₆" (42.5 x 30.0 cm.)

67 Giovanni Battista Tiepolo (1696-1770)
St. Jerome in the Desert Listening to
the Angels
Pen and brown ink, brown wash, heightened
with white, over black chalk on buff paper
16¾ʺ x 10⅞ʺ (42.5 x 27.6 cm.)

68 François Boucher (1703-1770)
Venus Reclining against a Dolphin
Black chalk heightened with white
9″ x 13½″ (22.8 x 34.3 cm.)

69 François Boucher (1703-1770)
    Landscape with a Rustic Bridge
    Black chalk heightened with white
    on buff paper
    8″ x 10¾″ (20.3 x 27.3 cm.)

70   Jean-Honoré Fragonard (1732-1806)
      Visit to the Nurse
      Chinese ink wash, heightened
      with watercolor
      12″ x 15″ (30.5 x 38.1 cm.)

71   Jean-Honoré Fragonard (1732-1806)
     The Little Preacher
     Brown wash over black chalk
     13¾″ x 18¼″ (34.9 x 46.7 cm.)

72   Jean-Honoré Fragonard (1732-1806)
Grandfather's Reprimand
Gray-brown wash over black chalk
13½″ x 17¾″ (34.3 x 45.1 cm.)

73 Jean-Honoré Fragonard (1732-1806)
    The Reading
    Brown wash, the corners rounded out
    11″ x 8¼″ (27.9 x 21 cm.)

74   Jean Auguste Dominique Ingres (1780-1867)
Mrs. Badham
Pencil on white wove paper
10¼″ x 8¼″ (26.0 x 21.0 cm.)

75 Jean François Millet (1814-1875)
    Peasants Resting
    Pastel
    16¾″ x 20¼″ (42.5 x 51.4 cm.)

76 Honoré Daumier (1808-1879)
The Pleading Lawyer
Watercolor, ink, and gouache
6¼″ x 8½″ (15.9 x 21.6 cm.)

77   Eugène Boudin (1824-1898)
     Beach Scene
     Pencil and watercolor
     $4\frac{5}{8}''$ x $9\frac{7}{16}''$ (11.7 x 24.0 cm.)

78   Camille Pissarro (1830-1903)
Montmorency Road
Pencil
9¼″ x 12⅜″ (23.5 x 31.4 cm.)

79   Camille Pissarro (1830-1903)
     Pea Harvest
     Watercolor and charcoal
     9″ x 11″ (22.8 x 27.9 cm.)

80 Edouard Manet (1832-1883)
    Man Wearing a Cloak (recto)
    Charcoal; 16″ x 8¾″ (40.6 x 19.7 cm.)
    Man Wearing a Cloak (verso)
    Charcoal

81   Edgar Degas (1834-1917)
Jacquet
Pastel
10¼″ x 8⅛″ (26.0 x 20.6 cm.)

82 Edgar Degas (1834-1917)
Laundresses Carrying Linen
Charcoal
17″ x 23″ (43.2 x 58.4 cm.)

83   Edgar Degas (1834-1917)
     Laundress Carrying Linen
     Pastel
     24″ x 36½″ (61.0 x 92.7 cm.)

84   Edgar Degas (1834-1917)
     Theater Box
     Pastel
     22″ x 16½″ (56.0 x 41.0 cm.)

85 Paul Cézanne (1839-1906)
    Study of the "Ecorché"
    Pencil
    6¼″ x 7″ (15.9 x 17.8 cm.)

86 Paul Cézanne (1839-1906)
Mont Ste. Victoire
Watercolor
6⁷/₁₆'' x 10⅝'' (16.4 x 27.0 cm.)

87 Claude Monet (1840-1926)
Two Women in a Boat
Pencil on paper
8½" x 10⅜" (21.6 x 26.4 cm.)

88   Odilon Redon (1840-1916)
      Vase of Flowers
      Pastel
      15¾″ x 12⅜″ (40.0 x 31.4 cm.)

89   Pierre Auguste Renoir (1841-1919)
Girlhood
Pencil
13⅜″ x 11⅜″ (34.0 x 28.9 cm.)

90   Paul Gauguin (1848-1903)
      Landscape at Pont-Aven
      Brush and ink
      12½″ x 17¼″ (31.8 x 43.8 cm.)

91 Paul Gauguin (1848-1903)
    Parau No Te Varau Ino (left)
    Tahitian Legend (right)
    Pen, brush, and India ink; two drawings on
    one sheet, side by side
    6″ x 3½″ (15.2 x 8.9 cm.)

92   Paul Gauguin (1848-1903)
      Tahitian Heads
      Pencil
      6⅜″ x 4″ (16.2 x 10.2 cm.)

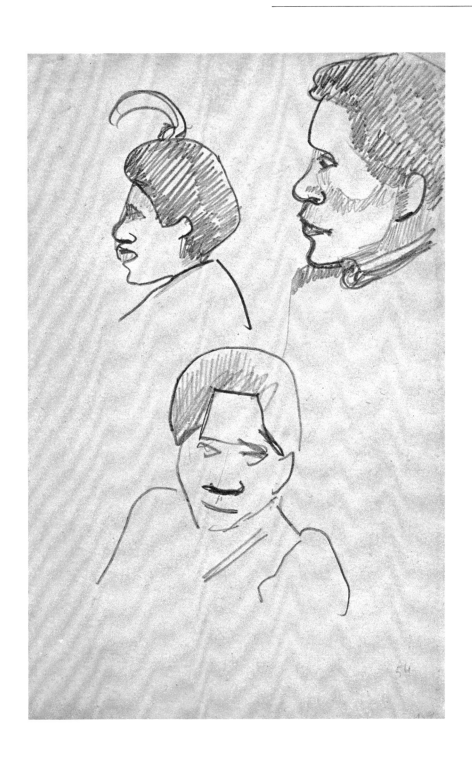

93A   *Breton Peasant*
     Pencil and crayon

On succeeding pages are sixteen sketches by
Paul Gauguin (1848-1903) from a sketchbook he
purchased in Rouen in 1884, and used intermittently
in Denmark and Brittany between 1884 and 1888. The
sketchbook contains 122 pages (6½″ x 4¼″;
16.5 x 10.8 cm.) including inside covers. Two of the
pages are blank, three contain miscellaneous notes, one
notes on color, eleven Gauguin's "Notes Synthétiques"
—his first written statement on art theory. The
remaining 105 pages are filled with 268 sketches of
landscapes, houses, animals, and people, mostly from
Brittany. Many of the images are used in pictures
of the same period.

93B *Little Breton Boy*
Pencil and crayon

93C *Little Breton Boy*
Pencil and crayon

93D   *Bridge at Pont-Aven* (?)
       Pencil and crayon

93E   *Two Breton Women*
       Pencil and crayon

93F *Head and Hand of a Monkey*
Pencil and crayon

93G *Little Breton Boy with Goose*
Pencil and crayon

93   Gauguin Sketchbook No. 16

93H   *Little Breton Boy with Pail*
      Pencil and crayon

93I   *Little Breton Boy with Pail*
      Pencil and crayon

93J *Sketches of a Child*
Ink

93K *Landscape*
Ink

93L *Head of a Child and Self-Portrait*
Ink

93M *Head of a Child and Head of a Man*
(probably self-portrait)
Ink

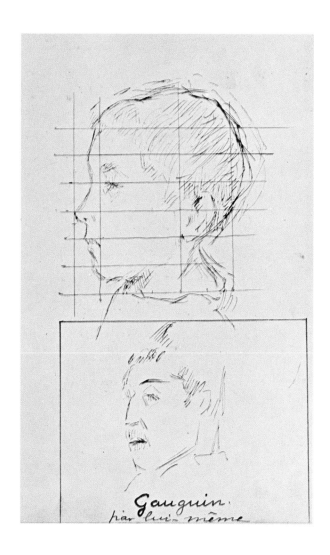

93N *Profile of Woman and Profile of Boy*
Ink

930 *Head of Woman, Tree, and*
Head of Man
Ink

93   Gauguin Sketchbook No. 16

  93P *Self-Portrait*
       Ink

94   Vincent van Gogh (1853-1890)
      Old Man Carrying a Bucket
      Pencil heightened with gray and black wash
      18¾″ x 8¼″ (47.6 x 21.0 cm.)

95   Vincent van Gogh (1853-1890)
The Zandmennik House
Charcoal
9″ x 11¾″ (22.9 x 29.8 cm.)

96   Vincent van Gogh (1853-1890)
The Magrot House, Cuesmes
Charcoal
9″ x 11¾″ (22.9 x 29.8 cm.)

97   Vincent van Gogh (1853-1890)
      Man Polishing a Boot
      Black chalk, pencil, heightened with white
      and gray wash
      19″ x 10½″ (48.3 x 26.7 cm.)

98   Vincent van Gogh (1853-1890)
The Weaver
Watercolor
12½″ x 17¾″ (31.8 x 45.1 cm.)

99   Henri-Edmond Cross (1856-1910)
     Cypresses
     Gouache
     9½″ x 13¼″ (24.1 x 33.7 cm.)

100 Georges Seurat (1859-1891)
Study after 'The Models'
Pen and ink
10¹/₁₆″ x 6⅜″ (26.0 x 16.5 cm.)

101 Henri de Toulouse-Lautrec (1864-1901)
Dance at the Moulin de la Galette
Ink and blue crayon on buff paper,
heightened with white
33½″ x 37½″ (85.1 x 95.3 cm.)

102 Pierre Bonnard (1867-1947)
Girl Drying Her Knees
Pencil
13″ x 9½″ (33.0 x 24.1 cm.)

103 Pablo Picasso (1881-   )
     Female Nude (recto)
     Pencil
     6½″ x 4″ (16.5 x 10.2 cm.)
     Young Man (verso)
     Pen and ink

Catalog of the Collection

1 Rembrandt van Rijn (1606-1669)
Portrait of a Man of the Raman Family, 1634
Oil on oval panel: 25½" x 19⅞" (64.8 x 50.5 cm.), enlarged
to rectangle 27⅛" x 21" (68.9 x 53.3 cm.)
Signed and dated lower right: Rembrandt fe 1634
Inscribed lower left: Aet. 47

Collections: The Raman family, Amsterdam; August de
Ridder, Schönberg near Cronberg; Kleinberger Galleries,
Paris; Ehrich Galleries, New York; Swiss private collector;
Julius Weitzner Galleries, New York; P. de Boer, Amsterdam;
H. Kohn, Wassenaar, Holland; H. Shickman Gallery,
New York; Los Angeles County Museum of Art (Frances
and Armand Hammer Purchase Fund, 1969)

Exhibitions: Frankfort-am-Main, Städelsches Kunstinstitut,
1911-1913 (following death of de Ridder, May 13, 1911);
New York, F. Kleinberger Galleries, *The Collection of
Pictures of the Late Herr A. de Ridder*, exhibition and private
sale Nov. 24-Dec. 15, 1913, no. 1 (repr. in cat. p. 32); Detroit
Institute of Arts, *Paintings by Rembrandt*, May 2-31, 1930,
no. 22 (repr. in cat.), (lent by the Ehrich Galleries,
New York); The Hague, Mauritshuis, Mar.-Apr., 1946,
no. 46; Basel, Katz Galerie, *Rembrandt Austellung*, July 24-
Sept. 30, 1948, no. 13 (repr. in cat.), (lent by Swiss private
collector); Raleigh, North Carolina Museum of Art, Nov. 16-
Dec. 30, 1956, no. 9 (repr. in cat.), (lent by Julius Weitzner,
New York); Memphis, Tennessee, Brooks Memorial Art
Gallery, *The Armand Hammer Collection*, Oct. 2-Dec. 30,
1969, no. 4 (repr. in cat.); Washington, D.C., Smithsonian
Institution, *The Armand Hammer Collection*, Mar. 20- May
17, 1970, no. 4 (repr. in cat. in color.)

Literature: W. R. Valentiner, *Rembrandt, des Meisters
Gemälde*, 3rd edition, (Klassiker der Kunst), Stuttgart/
Berlin: 1909, repr. p. 193 as "Portrait of a Man"; Wilhelm
Bode, *Die Gemäldegalerie des Herrn A. de Ridder*, Berlin:
Julius Bard, 1910, p. 4, 35, repr. pl. 1 as "Portrait of a Man
of the Raman Family"; Wilhelm Bode, *The Collection of
Pictures of the Late Herr A. de Ridder* (trans. Harry Virgin),
Berlin: Julius Bard, 1913, no. 1, repr. pl. 1; Hofstede de
Groot, *A Catalogue Raisonné of the Works of the Most
Eminent Dutch Painters of the Seventeenth Century*,
London: Macmillan, 1916, vol. VI, p. 347, no. 739 as "A
Man in a Large Slouch Hat, said to be a member of the
Raman family"; Sale catalog, *Catalogue des tableaux
anciens . . . composant la Galerie de feu M. A. de Ridder*,
Paris: Galerie Georges Petit, June 2, 1924, no. 55, repr.; A.
Bredius, *Rembrandt Gemälde*, Vienna: Phaidon, 1935,
no. 194; A. Bredius, *The Paintings of Rembrandt*, Vienna:
Phaidon, 1937, no. 194; Jakob Rosenberg, *Rembrandt*,
Cambridge: Harvard University Press, 1948, vol. I, p. 243
(concordance); Kurt Bauch, *Rembrandt Gemälde*, Berlin:
1966, de Gruyter, p. 19 (notes), no. 374, repr. no. 374; Horst
Gerson, *Rembrandt Paintings*, Amsterdam and New York:

Reynal & Co., 1968, p. 495, no. 168, repr. p. 289; Horst
Gerson (ed.), *Rembrandt, The Complete Edition of the
Paintings of Rembrandt by A. Bredius*, London: Phaidon,
1969, p. 564, no. 194, repr. p. 158

The sitter has been called a member of the Raman family
since, according to Bode, 1910, the painting came directly
from the old Amsterdam patrician family, Raman, to the
de Ridder collection. It had presumably been in that family
from the time it was painted. The picture does not appear in
the Rembrandt literature until Valentiner included it in the
third edition of the Klassiker der Kunst *Rembrandt* in 1909.
By that time it had already been enlarged from its original
shape to a rectangle. In subsequent literature (Hofstede de
Groot, 1916; Bauch, 1966; Gerson, 1968; Gerson-Bredius,
1969) the statement is made that the painting was originally
ten-sided. If that were true, the enlargement would follow a
simple decagonal pattern. X-rays show, however, a quite
irregular twelve-sided pattern which suggests that the
painting was originally an oval, approximately the same as
that shown in the present frame. Cleaning has also shown
the present original to be oval rather than decagonal. This is
clearly visible in the reproduction of Bredius, 1937.

Bode, 1910, noted the extraordinarily fine state of
preservation of the picture. This has been attested in a recent
cleaning at the Los Angeles County Museum of Art. *The
Portrait of a Lady in a Broad Ruff*, 1636, reported as in the
collection of Kinnaird, Rossie Priory (Bredius no. 354) has
been considered in the Rembrandt literature from Hofstede
de Groot on to be a companion to the Hammer portrait.

2 Peter Paul Rubens (1577-1640)
Young Woman with Curly Hair, ca. 1618-1620
Oil on panel
17 1/16" x 13 3/16" (43.3 x 33.5 cm.), enlarged to
26⅜" x 20⅝" (67 x 52.4 cm.)

Collections: Schamp d'Aveschoot, Ghent (recorded 1830);
Duc d'Arenberg and descendants, Brussels and later South of
France (purchased 1840 at Schamp sale); Edward Speelman,
London (bought 1959 from present Duke); Jean Davray,
Paris

Exhibition: Memphis, Tennessee, Brooks Memorial Art
Gallery, *The Armand Hammer Collection*, Oct. 2-Dec. 30,
1969, no. 2 (repr. color on cat. cover; repr. in cat.);
Washington, D. C., Smithsonian Institution, *The Armand
Hammer Collection*, Mar. 20-May 17, 1970, no. 2 (repr. color
on cat. cover; repr. in cat. in color); Smithsonian Institution
Traveling Exhibition Service, *The Armand Hammer
Collection*, Kansas City, Missouri, William Rockhill Nelson
Gallery of Art, June 30-Aug. 2, 1970, New Orleans,
Louisiana, Isaac Delgado Museum of Art, Aug. 15-Sept. 20,
1970, Columbus, Ohio, Columbus Gallery of Fine Arts, Oct.
9-Nov. 1, 1970, Little Rock, Arkansas, Arkansas Art Center,

Nov. 21, 1970-Jan. 12, 1971; San Francisco, California, California Palace of the Legion of Honor, *The Armand Hammer Collection*, Feb. 11-Mar. 14, 1971; Oklahoma City, Oklahoma, Oklahoma Art Center, *The Armand Hammer Collection*, June 15-July 11, 1971; San Diego, California, Fine Arts Gallery of San Diego, *The Armand Hammer Collection*, July 23-Sept. 5, 1971

Literature: John Smith, *Catalogue Raisonné of the Works of the Most Eminent Dutch, Flemish and French Painters*, vol. II (Rubens), London: Smith & Son, 1830, pp. 260-261, no. 881; and vol. IX (Supplement), 1842, p. 330, no. 317; Sale catalog, *Catalogue des tableaux . . . composant la galerie de M. Schamp d'Aveschoot, de Gand*, Sept. 14, 1840, p. 2; Max Rooses, *L'oeuvre de P. P. Rubens*, Antwerp, 1886-1892, vol. IV, pp. 138, 290, no. 1088; J. Nève, "Quelques Portraits de la Galerie d'Arenberg," *Annales de l'Académie Royale d'Archéologie de Belgique*, Antwerp: vol. V, 4th series, vol. X (1897), pp. 275, 276; Max Rooses, "Oeuvres de Rubens—Addenda," *Bulletin Rubens*, Antwerp: vol. 5 (1909), pp. 83-84; Rudolf Oldenbourg, *P. P. Rubens*, Munich, Berlin, 1922, p. 142; Ludwig Burchard, "Portrait of a Young Woman with Curly Hair by Peter Paul Rubens," manuscript report on Arenberg-Hammer painting, ca. 1960; Douglas Cooper (ed.), *Great Private Collections*, New York: Macmillan, 1963, repr. p. 257; Michael Jaffé, manuscript letter to Roland Balay, M. Knoedler & Co., New York, dated: Cambridge University, Feb. 3, 1967; Michael Harvard, "Portrait of a Girl with Curly Hair by Rubens," manuscript report on the Arenberg-Hammer and Morris paintings, London: March, 1969; Michael Jaffé, "The Girl with the Golden Hair," *Apollo*, vol. XC, no. 92, Oct. 1969, pp. 310-313, repr. in color p. 311

The portrait as Rubens painted it was only the head and shoulders of the young woman. A seventeenth-century copy in the museum in Cassel shows the portrait in its original size. Sometime in the seventeenth or early eighteenth century the bevelled edge, about one inch all around, was trimmed off and the painting was set into a larger panel a little towards the top and right of center. The new panel seems to have been an oval, to which wedges were then or later added to make the present rectangle.

The identity of the sitter is not known. Jaffé believes that the painting is a study rather than a formal portrait. According to Burchard, Rubens made a second study of the same girl but in a more frontal pose (Munich, Alte Pinakothek, no. 793 in cat.; exhibited in Bamberg Museum in 1934). The Munich painting measures 18⅞" x 14½", approximately the same as the Hammer painting originally and, in Burchard's opinion, was probably painted at the same sitting.

The Hammer picture must have been extraordinarily popular in the seventeenth and eighteenth centuries, for at least six early repetitions of it are known: the Cassel copy of the original before enlargement (canvas 17¼" x 13¾", no. 89 in cat. of 1888); four repetitions of the present enlarged image: Dresden Museum (panel 25¼" x 19½", no. 964A in cat. of 1908, repr. Adolf Rosenberg, *P. P. Rubens, des Meisters Gemälde* [Klassiker der Kunst], second edition, Stuttgart/Leipzig, 1906, p. 373); Leningrad, Hermitage (canvas said to have been transferred from panel 26" x 21¼", no. 577 in cat. of 1901, with additional drapery across chest and near shoulder); Althrop, The Earl Spencer Collection (with two jeweled clasps holding bodice); Kiel, Prof. Götz Martins (panel 22⅞" x 16⅛"), similar to Spencer portrait; and a sixth painting still further enlarged in the collection of John C. Morris, Richmond, Surrey. The Morris painting (panel 28" x 23¼") (repr. in Rudolf Oldenbourg, *P. P. Rubens, des Meisters Gemälde* [Klassiker der Kunst] fourth edition, Berlin/Leipzig, 1921, p. 201) has a slightly lower neckline and extends the torso almost to the hips. Michael Jaffé believes that all these repetitions of the enlarged picture were made after Rubens' death and that only the Hammer picture is an original by Rubens.

3   Peter Paul Rubens (1577-1640)
The Israelites Gathering Manna in the Desert, 1625-1628
Oil on panel: 25½" x 20¾" (64.8 x 52.7 cm.)

Collections: Isabella Clara Eugenia, Archduchess of the Spanish Netherlands, Brussels; Philip IV and Charles II of Spain; Don Francisco Casimiro Pimentel, Conde de Benavente, who in 1700, following the death of Charles II, received this and the other paintings from the Royal Collections kept in the Pieza de las Furias for himself and his successors; Dukes of Pastrana, Madrid, by inheritance from the Counts of Benavente; Emile Pacully, Paris (acquired from Duc de Pastrana, Madrid, probably at sale of 1888); Baron Robert Gendebien, Brussels (acquired from A. Stein, dealer, Paris); Rosenberg & Stiebel, New York; Los Angeles County Museum of Art (Frances and Armand Hammer Purchase Fund, 1969)

Exhibitions: Rotterdam, Boymans Museum, *Olieverfschelsen van Rubens*, Dec. 19, 1953-Feb. 14, 1954, no. 73 (cat. by E. Haverkamp Bergemann, pp. 85, 86, repr. pl. 63); Bordeaux, May 19-July 31, 1954, *Flandres, Espagne, Portugal du XVᵉ au XVIIᵉ Siècle*, 1954, no. 80 (p. 83 in cat.); Brussels, Musées Royaux des Beaux-Arts de Belgique, *Le Siècle de Rubens*, Oct. 15-Dec. 12, 1965, no. 225 (pp. 215, 216 in cat. by Leo van Puyvelde, repr.); Memphis, Tennessee, Brooks Memorial Art Gallery, *The Armand Hammer Collection*, Oct. 2-Dec. 30, 1969, no. 3 (repr. in cat.); Washington, D. C., Smithsonian Institution, *The Armand Hammer Collection*, Mar. 20-May 17, 1970, no. 3 (repr. in cat. in color)

Literature: Max Rooses, *L'Oeuvre de Pierre-Paul Rubens*, Antwerp, 1886-1892, vol. I, p. 73; Max Rooses, "De

Verzameling Pacully te Paris," *Onze Kunst*, 1903, pp. 121-122; Virgile Josz, "La Collection Emile Pacully," *Les Arts*, 2nd year, no. 16, Apr. 1903, p. 35, repr. p. 36; Sale catalog, *Collection Emile Pacully, tableaux anciens et modernes*, Paris: Galerie Georges Petit, May 4, 1903, pp. 62-63, repr. with added garland; N. Sentenac y Cantanas, *La pintura en Madrid desde sus origenes hasta el siglo XIX*, Madrid, 1907, pp. 78 ff.: History and inventory of Pastrana collection; Sale catalog, *Tableaux . . . dépendant de la succession de Monsieur E. Pacully*, Paris: Hôtel Drouot, July 5, 1938, no. 28, repr. with added garland, as by Rubens and Jan Brueghel (This and several other pictures from the 1903 sale were apparently bought back by the owner and kept through his lifetime); Leo von Puyvelde, *Les Esquisses de Rubens*, Basel: Holbein, 1940, p. 31, no. 7 (Engl. trans. London, 1947, p. 29); Egbert Haverkamp Begemann, "Rubens Schetsen," *Bulletin Museum Boymans Rotterdam*, vol. V, no. 1, Mar. 1954, p. 9, repr. p. 11; Victor H. Elbern, "Die Rubensteppiche des Kölner Domes, ihre Geschichte und ihre Stellung im Zyklus Triumph der Eucharistie," *Kölner Domblatt*, vol. X, 1955, pp. 74-75, repr. pl. 29

About 1625 the Archduchess Isabella Clara Eugenia, daughter of Philip II of Spain and ruler of the Spanish Netherlands, commissioned Rubens to produce eleven huge paintings and several smaller ones to be used as cartoons (full size patterns) for a series of tapestries glorifying the Eucharist which she wished to present to the Convent of the Descalzas Reales (Franciscan Clarissa Nuns) in Madrid. The subjects were: four Old Testament prefigurations of the New Testament Eucharist, one of which was the Israelites gathering manna in the desert; two of the Evangelists and Eucharistic teachers and defenders; and five Eucharistic triumphs. The first series of tapestries made in Brussels was sent to the Convent in Madrid in July 1628. A second series is now in the Cathedral of Cologne. Other individual panels were woven.

In the preparation of the cartoons Rubens first painted rough sketches in grisaille, then full-color sketches *(modelli)* which were enlarged by the master and his shop to the desired size of the tapestry. The first sketch for *The Israelites Gathering Manna in the Desert* is a panel 5¾" x 4⅞" in the Musée Bonnat, Bayonne. In it Moses is in the background of a composition with a strong movement from left to right. In preparing the Los Angeles *modello* Rubens centralized the composition, confining it between Moses on the right and the woman with the child who turns towards center on the left. The woman is adapted from the woman with a jug in the Raphael *Fire in the Borgo* in the Vatican; other elements in both the grisaille and the *modello* are related to a Rubens drawing in the Louvre (Lugt no. 1038, fig. 52, also repr. Elbern, 1958, fig. 12) after a Giulio Romano *Gathering of the Manna*. Employing Renaissance elements and classic

compositional limits, Rubens has filled his stage with a dynamic movement and counter-movement of form, light, and psychology not possible before the seventeenth century.

In 1648 Philip IV asked that the large cartoons and "other small paintings" for the Triumph of the Eucharist series be sent to Madrid. It is assumed by Rubens scholars that the sketches which were in the Royal Collections of Spain in the late seventeenth century, including the Los Angeles *modello*, were sent at that time. Presumably before 1648, the Los Angeles *modello* was set into a larger panel and surrounded by a garland of flowers and fruits. Max Rooses' *(Onze Kunst*, 1903) attribution of the garland, formerly called Jan Brueghel, to Pieter Gysels (1621-1690), would imply a date in the late forties. The *modello* with the garland is reproduced in the two Pacully sale catalogs and in *Les Arts*, 1903. The enlargement was removed and the painting restored to its original size after the sale of 1938.

The Los Angeles *modello* was separated from the other Triumph of the Eucharist *modelli* now in the Prado when it was inherited by the Conde de Benavente. The Los Angeles *modello* had presumably been sold to Pacully before the Duchess of Pastrana presented a number of Rubens sketches for the Torre de la Parada from the same Benavente-Pastrana inheritance to the Prado on May 28, 1889 (Prado nos. 2038-2040).

The large cartoon (canvas, 192" x 163") made from the Los Angeles *modello* was one of six cartoons sent in 1648 to Philip IV. He presented the six to Olivares, who placed them in his small family church at Loeches, near Madrid. They were removed by French troops during the Napoleonic invasions. Two became the property of the Louvre; four, including *The Israelites Gathering Manna in the Desert*, were sold in 1818 to the Duke of Westminster and in 1928 to John Ringling for the Ringling Museum in Sarasota, Florida (repr. William E. Suida, *A Catalogue of Paintings in the John and Mable Ringling Museum of Art*, Sarasota, 1949, pp. 178-183). A copy of the Los Angeles *modello* is in the Museum of Doornik (Tournai). A School of Rubens drawing of the composition is in the Louvre (Lugt no. 1127).

The most concise study of the series in English is Julius Held, "Rubens' Triumph of the Eucharist and the *Modello* in Louisville," *J. B. Speed Art Museum Bulletin*, vol. XXVI, no. 3 (Feb. 1968). The most exhaustive studies are Elias Tormo, *En las Descalzas Reales de Madrid*, Tomo II, Fasiculo II, "Los Tapices: La Apoteosis Eucarística de Rubens," Madrid: Junta de Iconografía Nacional, 1945; and Victor H. Elbern, "Die Rubensteppiche des Kölner Domes, ihre Geschichte und ihre Stellung in Zyklus Triumph der Eucharistie," *Kölner Domblatt*, X, 1955, pp. 43-88; XIV/XV, 1958, p. 121 ff.; XXI/XXII, 1963, pp. 77 ff.

4　Jean-Honoré Fragonard (1732-1806)
The Education of the Virgin, 1748-1752
Oil on panel: 11¹³/₁₆" x 9⅝" (30.0 x 24.4 cm.)

Collections: J. B. P. Lebrun, Paris; Fontaine, Paris; Charles T. . . ., Paris; Camille Groult, Paris; Wildenstein & Co., Inc., New York; Mr. and Mrs. Henry R. Luce, New York

Exhibitions: New Haven, Yale University Art Gallery, *Pictures Collected by Yale Alumni*, May 8-June 18, 1956, no. 19 (repr. in cat.); Memphis, Tennessee, Brooks Memorial Art Gallery, *The Armand Hammer Collection*, Oct. 2-Dec. 30, 1969, no. 5 (repr. in cat.); Washington, D. C., Smithsonian Institution, *The Armand Hammer Collection*, Mar. 20-May 17, 1970, no. 5 (repr. in cat. in color); Smithsonian Institution Traveling Exhibition Service, *The Armand Hammer Collection*, Kansas City, Missouri, William Rockhill Nelson Gallery of Art, June 30-Aug. 2, 1970, New Orleans, Louisiana, Isaac Delgado Museum of Art, Aug. 15-Sept. 20, 1970, Columbus, Ohio, Columbus Gallery of Fine Arts, Oct. 9-Nov. 1, 1970, Little Rock, Arkansas, Arkansas Art Center, Nov. 21, 1970-Jan. 12, 1971; San Francisco, California, California Palace of the Legion of Honor, *The Armand Hammer Collection*, Feb. 11-Mar. 14, 1971; Oklahoma City, Oklahoma, Oklahoma Art Center, *The Armand Hammer Collection*, June 15-July 11, 1971

Literature: Sale catalog, *Catalogue d'objets rares et curieux, provenant du Cabinet et Fonds de Marchandises de M. Lebrun par cessation de Commerce*, Paris: Galerie de M. Lebrun, Sept. 29, 1806, no. 150; Pierre de Nolhac, *J-H Fragonard*, Paris: Goupil & Cie., 1906, p. 164; Georges Wildenstein, *The Paintings of Fragonard*, Phaidon, 1960, p. 195, no. 18, repr. pl. 1

Fragonard used this subject for at least three paintings: an unfinished picture in a private collection, 35½" x 28⅜" (Wildenstein, no. 17); another version in the California Palace of the Legion of Honor, San Francisco, 32¼" x 45⅝" at present, but probably cut down between 1793 and 1806 (Wildenstein, no. 19); and the Hammer picture. They were all executed presumably between 1748 and 1752 when the young Fragonard was a pupil of Boucher. The Hammer picture, which has the freshness and freedom of execution of a sketch, seems to be the artist's first statement of the image. It may then have become the model for the larger unfinished picture which corresponds closely to it in composition. The San Francisco version, more academic in its drawing, modeling, and light, seems to be the final distillation of the idea.

5   Francisco Goya (1746-1828)
El Pelele, ca. 1791
Oil on canvas: 14" x 9⅛" (35.6 x 23.2 cm.)

Collections: Doña Beatriz Sánchez de la Fuente de Lafora, Madrid; Don Juan de Lafora, Madrid; M. Knoedler & Co., New York; Mr. and Mrs. Henry R. Luce, New York

Exhibitions: Madrid, Sociedad Española de Amigos del Arte,

Bocetos y Estudias para Pinturas y Esculturas, May-June 1949, no. 109, catalog by F. J. Sánchez-Canton; New Haven, Yale University Art Gallery, *Pictures Collected by Yale Alumni*, May 8-June 18, 1956, no. 29 (repr. in cat.); Memphis, Tennessee, Brooks Memorial Art Gallery, *The Armand Hammer Collection*, Oct. 2-Dec. 30, 1969, no. 6 (repr. in cat.); Washington, D. C., Smithsonian Institution, *The Armand Hammer Collection*, Mar. 20-May 17, 1970, no. 6 (repr. in cat. in color); Smithsonian Institution Traveling Exhibition Service, *The Armand Hammer Collection*, Kansas City, Missouri, William Rockhill Nelson Gallery of Art, June 30-Aug. 2, 1970, New Orleans, Louisiana, Isaac Delgado Museum of Art, Aug. 15-Sept. 20, 1970, Columbus, Ohio, Columbus Gallery of Fine Arts, Oct. 9-Nov. 1, 1970, Little Rock, Arkansas, Arkansas Art Center, Nov. 21, 1970-Jan. 12, 1971; San Francisco, California, California Palace of the Legion of Honor, *The Armand Hammer Collection*, Feb. 11-Mar. 14, 1971; Oklahoma City, Oklahoma, Oklahoma Art Center, *The Armand Hammer Collection*, June 15-July 11, 1971

Literature: August L. Mayer, *Francisco de Goya*, Munich: F. Bruckmann, 1923, p. 210, no. 570a, Engl. trans. London and Toronto: J. M. Dent, 1924, p. 176, no. 570a; Valentín de Sambricio, *Tápices de Goya*, Madrid: Patrimonio Nacional, Archivo General del Palacio, 1946, p. 273, no. 58a, repr. pl. CLXXXIV

In 1776 Goya began a series of oil paintings of Spanish popular life to be used as cartoons for forty-six tapestries by the Real Fábrica de Tápices de Santa Bárbara in Madrid. The large cartoons are preserved in the Prado. *El Pelele* (Prado no. 802, 105" x 63"), painted about 1791, was one of the last three cartoons delivered. The tapestry, today in the Palace of El Prado, was executed in 1793. There are two known *bocetos* for the Prado cartoon, one in the collection of Mrs. R. H. Kress (17½" x 10"), the other in this collection. The Hammer picture is presumably the first concept of the subject, with its freely sketched figures and the pentimenti in the straw man. Especially noticeable is the change in the position of the left foreleg. The group stands in an open space before a wall at the left and with the slightest indication of foliage at the right. In the Kress picture the figures are close to those in the Hammer picture; the primary difference is in the development of a more airy and spacious background. The wall has receded and a large shrub has grown between it and the figure group to indicate the extension of space. In the Prado cartoon the straw man has assumed a new and more limp position, the dresses and features of the four girls have been considerably elaborated, the wall has now become a palace in the far distance, and delicate shrubbery creates a broad and deep landscape so that the straw man can be more effectively silhouetted against the sky.

This may well have been one of the "Diez y seis bocetos pequeños de los tápices" listed in the inventory of the personal property of Francisco Goya in Madrid inherited by his son Javier Goya (Inventory published in X. Despartmet Fitz-Gerald, *L'Oeuvre peint de Goya*, Paris: F. de Nobele, 1928-50, text vol. I, pp. 53-54).

6 Théodore Géricault (1791-1824)
Portrait of a Gentleman
Oil on canvas: 25⅝" x 21¼" (65.1 x 54.0 cm.)
Signed lower left: T.G.

Collections: Christie, Manson & Woods, London; Le Bohélec, Paris; Sale, Paris, Galerie Charpentier, June 16, 1955; Drs. Fritz and Peter Nathan, Zurich

Exhibitions: Winterthur, Kunstmuseum, *Théodore Géricault*, 1953, no. 92; Los Angeles County Museum of Art, *Géricault*, Oct. 12-Dec. 12, 1971, no. 3 (repr.), also The Detroit Institute of Arts, Jan. 23-Mar. 7, 1972, and Philadelphia Museum of Art, Mar. 30-May 14, 1972

Literature: C. Clément, *Géricault, étude biographique et critique*, Paris, 1867 (3rd edition, enlarged, 1879); F. H. Lem, "Géricault portraitiste," *L'Arte*, Jan.-June, 1963, p. 68

Signed "T.G." at the lower left, this picture was traditionally supposed to be a portrait of the composer F. A. Boïeldieu (1775-1834) although it does not bear any very pronounced resemblance to his known portraits. Of unusually tight and careful finish, the portrait is to be considered one of Géricault's master copies, executed probably about 1810-12, after a slightly earlier work by a portraitist in the vicinity of Boilly or the elder Isabey. Other, equally deceptive copies by him are known (eg., the copy after H. Rigaud's *Portrait of the Mother of the Artist*, private collection, Paris).

7 Camille Corot (1796-1875)
Portrait of a Girl, ca. 1860
Oil on canvas: 12¼" x 9³/₁₆" (32.1 x 24.3 cm.)
Signed upper right: Corot

Collections: Emile Bernheim, Paris; André Pacitti, Paris

Exhibitions: Smithsonian Institution Traveling Exhibition Service, *The Armand Hammer Collection*, no. 95 (repr. in cat. supplement), Kansas City, Missouri, William Rockhill Nelson Gallery of Art, June 30-Aug. 2, 1970, New Orleans, Louisiana, Isaac Delgado Museum of Art, Aug. 15-Sept. 20, 1970, Columbus, Ohio, Columbus Gallery of Fine Arts, Oct. 9-Nov. 1, 1970, Little Rock, Arkansas, Arkansas Art Center, Nov. 21, 1970-Jan. 12, 1971; San Francisco, California, California Palace of the Legion of Honor, *The Armand Hammer Collection*, Feb. 11-Mar. 14, 1971; Oklahoma City, Oklahoma, Oklahoma Art Center, *The Armand Hammer Collection*, June 15-July 11, 1971; San Diego, California,

Fine Arts Gallery of San Diego, *The Armand Hammer Collection*, July 23-Sept. 5, 1971

Literature: André Schoeller and Jean Dieterle, *Corot, Deuxième Supplément à "L'Oeuvre de Corot" par Alfred Robaut et Moreau-Nélaton*, Editions Floury, Paris: Quatre Chemins, 1956, no. 28

Degas was among the first to appreciate Corot's abilities as a figure painter, abilities that have generally gone unrecognized because of the popularity of the artist's landscapes. Toward the end of his life Corot's figures became generalized into national or allegorical types, and individualized portraits such as this became increasingly rare. During the same period the artist showed a marked predilection for a Leonardesque type, its softly-modeled face gazing abstractedly outward, its arms folded across each other. The Louvre's *Woman with the Pearl* is the best example of this type, and the 1962 *Figures de Corot* catalog suggests a relationship with both the *Mona Lisa* and the *Belle Ferronnière*. A portrait of a young woman from the Hirschland Collection represents an intermediate compositional step between the *Woman with the Pearl* and this picture.

8 Camille Corot (1796-1875)
Medieval Ruins, ca. 1828-1830
Oil on canvas, mounted on board: 9" x 12" (23.0 x 30.5 cm.)
Lower right: Stamp, Vente Corot; red wax seal of the Vente Corot, verso

Collections: Vente Corot, 1875, no. 329; Comte Armand Doria (Sale, Paris, May 5, 1899, no. 108); Madame Lazard, Paris; Mr. and Mrs. Eliot Hodgkin, London (Sale, London, Sotheby & Co., Apr. 29, 1964, no. 35A, repr.); Norton Simon, Los Angeles (Sale, New York, Parke-Bernet Galleries, Inc., May 5, 1971, no. 2, repr.)

Exhibitions: Paris, Musée Jacquemart André, *Le Second Empire*, 1957, no. 62; Chicago, The Art Institute, *Corot*, 1960, no. 23; London, Marlborough Fine Art, Ltd., *Corot*, 1963, no. 10; Oklahoma City, Oklahoma, Oklahoma Art Center, *The Armand Hammer Collection*, June 15-July 11, 1971; San Diego, California, Fine Arts Gallery of San Diego, *The Armand Hammer Collection*, July 23-Sept. 5, 1971

Literature: Alfred Robaut, *L'Oeuvre de Corot*, Paris: H. Floury, 1905, vol. II, p. 75, no. 212, repr.; Sale catalog, *Impressionist and Modern Paintings, Drawings, and Sculpture*, London: Sotheby & Co., Apr. 29, 1964, no. 35A, repr.; Sale catalog, *Highly Important 19th and 20th Century Paintings, Drawings & Sculpture from the Private Collection of Norton Simon*, New York: Parke-Bernet Galleries, Inc., May 5, 1971, no. 2, repr.

Catalogued in the Vente Corot as "Pierrefonds, au pied du Château," this picture has been said by Robaut to be a view of Arques-la-Bataille. The latter site, near Dieppe, contains the ruins of an eleventh-century fortress built by an uncle of William the Conqueror. The former, near Compiègne, was the site of a fourteenth-century chateau, the remains of which were completely rebuilt by Viollet-le-Duc in the mid-nineteenth century at the order of Napoleon III. Robaut lists two views of Arques painted by Corot about the time of this sketch, three drawings and two paintings of Pierrefonds. Of the latter, three were executed in the 1840s and two in the 1860s. The present picture was probably painted between Corot's first two trips to Italy, that is about 1828-1830. It combines his interest in subjects observed on the spot with the luminism he had developed in the south. In this case the evenness of the northern French light produces two large tonal areas, a light sky and a darker foreground, forecasting the softness of Corot's late work and contrasting with the sharper illumination of his Italian pictures.

9   Camille Corot (1796-1875)
     Harvester Under Trees, ca. 1829
     Oil on canvas: 15 13/16" x 12" (40.1 x 30.5 cm.)
     Lower left: Stamp, Vente Corot

Collections: M. Mauritz, Paris; Adrien Meunier, Paris; Galerie Daber, Paris

Exhibitions: New York, Hammer Galleries, *40th Anniversary Loan Exhibition, 1928-1968,* Nov. 7-Dec. 7, 1968, p. 20 (repr.); Memphis, Tennessee, Brooks Memorial Art Gallery, Oct. 2-Dec. 30, 1969, no. 7 (repr.); Washington, D. C., Smithsonian Institution, *The Armand Hammer Collection,* Mar. 20-May 17, 1970, no. 7 (repr. in cat. in color); Smithsonian Institution Traveling Exhibition Service, *The Armand Hammer Collection,* Kansas City, Missouri, William Rockhill Nelson Gallery of Art, June 30-Aug. 2, 1970, New Orleans, Louisiana, Isaac Delgado Museum of Art, Aug. 15-Sept. 20, 1970, Columbus, Ohio, Columbus Gallery of Fine Arts, Oct. 9-Nov. 1, 1970, Little Rock, Arkansas, Arkansas Art Center, Nov. 21, 1970-Jan. 12, 1971, San Francisco, California, California Palace of the Legion of Honor, *The Armand Hammer Collection,* Feb. 11-Mar. 14, 1971; Oklahoma City, Oklahoma, Oklahoma Art Center, *The Armand Hammer Collection,* June 15-July 11, 1971

Literature: Alfred Robaut, *L'Oeuvre de Corot,* Paris: H. Floury, 1905, vol. II, p. 74, no. 219 bis, vol. IV, p. 230, no. 323 bis, (sketch by A. Robaut from Posthumous Sale Catalog, Hôtel Drouot, May 26, 1875); François Daulte, "Hammer en dix chefs-d'oeuvre," *Connaissance des Arts,* Sept. 1970, pp. 82-83, repr. in color

Executed at about the same time as the Hammer *Medieval Ruins* and in a similar rapid style, this picture is considerably darker in tonality and for that reason more suggestive of the work of the Barbizon school. Only the

harvester's white shirt and the light patch of sky relieve the rich greens and browns of the shadows. The serpentine wall connecting foreground and middleground and the diagonally recessive row of trees are unusual devices for Corot. They provide a somewhat more obvious pictorial scaffolding than one finds in the painter's later work. The subject is a scene of unposed action, also unusual for Corot.

10   Camille Corot (1796-1875)
     Distant View of Mantes Cathedral, ca. 1855-1860
     Oil on canvas: 22 1/16" x 18 1/16" (56.0 x 45.9 cm.)
     Signed lower left: Corot

Collections: M. Knoedler & Co., Paris, 1899; Galerie Georges Petit, Paris (Sale, Paris, Hôtel Drouot, Apr. 27, 1933, no. 49); M. Damidot; Ferdinand Blumenthal, Paris; Léfèvre Gallery, London; Count Pecci-Blunt, Paris; C. W. Boise, London

Exhibitions: Paris, Galerie Georges Petit, *Exposition Vingts Peintures du XIXe Siècle, Cent Chefs-d'Oeuvre de l'Ecole Française,* 1910, no. 8; New York, M. Knoedler & Co., *The Landscape in French Painting, XIXth-XXth Centuries,* 1910; Amsterdam, *Les Peintures Françaises aux XIXe et XXe Siècle,* Apr.-May, 1931; New York, Hammer Galleries, *40th Anniversary Loan Exhibition, 1928-1968,* Nov. 7-Dec. 7, 1968 (repr. in cat. in color p. 19); Memphis, Tennessee, Brooks Memorial Art Gallery, *The Armand Hammer Collection,* Oct. 2-Dec. 30, 1969, no. 14 (repr. in cat.); Washington, D. C., Smithsonian Institution, *The Armand Hammer Collection,* Mar. 20-May 17, 1970, no. 14 (repr. in cat. in color); Smithsonian Institution Traveling Exhibition Service, *The Armand Hammer Collection,* Kansas City, Missouri, William Rockhill Nelson Gallery of Art, June 30-Aug. 2, 1970, New Orleans, Louisiana, Isaac Delgado Museum of Art, Aug. 15-Sept. 20, 1970, Columbus, Ohio, Columbus Gallery of Fine Arts, Oct. 9-Nov. 1, 1970, Little Rock, Arkansas, Arkansas Art Center, Nov. 21, 1970-Jan. 12, 1971; San Francisco, California, California Palace of the Legion of Honor, *The Armand Hammer Collection,* Feb. 11-Mar. 14, 1971; Oklahoma City, Oklahoma, Oklahoma Art Center, *The Armand Hammer Collection,* June 15-July 11, 1971; San Diego, California, Fine Arts Gallery of San Diego, *The Armand Hammer Collection,* July 23-Sept. 5, 1971

Literature: Alfred Robaut, *L'Oeuvre de Corot,* Paris: H. Floury, 1905, vol. II, p. 264, no. 818, repr. p. 265; L. Roger-Milès, *Chefs-d'Oeuvre de l'Ecole Française,* Paris: Georges Petit, 1911, repr. p. 103; Horace Shipp, *The French Masters,* London: Samson Low, Marston & Co., repr. p. 112; *Gazette des Beaux-Arts,* Apr. 21, 1933, repr. p. 3; *Gazette des Beaux-Arts,* May 5, 1933, p. 6; *Art News,* Apr. 8, 1933, repr. p. 8; Germain Bazin, *Corot,* Paris, 1950, pl. 92; Radolphe Walter, "Jean Baptiste Corot et la Cathédrale

Restaurée," *Gazette des Beaux-Arts*, Apr. 1966, pp. 217-228, repr.; *Burlington Magazine*, Apr. 1968, repr. p. VII; *Connoisseur*, Aug. 1968, repr. p. XIV; Sale catalog, *Impressionist and Modern Paintings, Drawings and Sculpture—Various Owners*, London: Sotheby & Co., Apr. 24, 1968, no. 61, repr.

Mantes (Mantes-la-jolie), a small town east of Paris notable for its magnificent church designed by Eudas de Montreuil, architect of Nôtre Dame at Paris, was painted many times by Corot between the early 1840s and the 1860s. He particularly favored its church and the bridge across the Seine as motifs. The present picture is not dissimilar to one in Reims taken from a slightly different viewpoint (Robaut 1522) although the composition is stronger by virtue of the placement of the trees and the log lying in the foreground. Two drawings in horizontal format (Robaut 817, 1519) were apparently made from the same spot. The disproportion in the towers of the church has led Walter to point out that the painting must have been executed during the rebuilding of the south tower from 1859-1860. He convincingly suggests that it dates to May 1859 when Corot was at nearby Rosny. The tonality of the picture is somewhat lighter and more even than one is used to from Corot, although he has been careful to add his usual small touch of red to spark the blue-green of the overall composition.

11 Camille Corot (1796-1875)
Grape Harvest at Sèvres, ca. 1865
Oil on canvas: 16⅞" x 29⅜" (42.8 x 74.6 cm.)
Signed lower left: Corot

Collections: Surville Collection, Paris, 1875; Dr. Seymour, Paris, 1888; P. H. Hodges (acquired from Reichard & Co.); Sale, Chickering Hall, New York, Feb. 21, 1895; A. H. Alker, New York

Exhibitions: Paris, Ecole des Beaux-Arts, 1875, no. 112 (lent by Mr. Surville); Memphis, Tennessee, Brooks Memorial Art Gallery, *The Armand Hammer Collection*, Oct. 2-Dec. 30, 1969, no. 16 (repr. in cat.); Washington, D. C., Smithsonian Institution, *The Armand Hammer Collection*, Mar. 20-May 17, 1970, no. 16 (repr. in cat. in color); Smithsonian Institution Traveling Exhibition Service, *The Armand Hammer Collection*, Kansas City, Missouri, William Rockhill Nelson Gallery of Art, June 30-Aug. 2, 1970, New Orleans, Louisiana, Isaac Delgado Museum of Art, Aug. 15-Sept. 20, 1970, Columbus, Ohio, Columbus Gallery of Fine Arts, Oct. 9-Nov. 1, 1970, Little Rock, Arkansas, Arkansas Art Center, Nov. 21, 1970-Jan. 12, 1971; San Francisco, California, California Palace of the Legion of Honor, *The Armand Hammer Collection*, Feb. 11-Mar. 14, 1971; Oklahoma City, Oklahoma, Oklahoma Art Center, *The Armand Hammer Collection*, June 15-July 11, 1971; San Diego, California, Fine Arts Gallery of San Diego,

The Armand Hammer Collection, July 23-Sept. 5, 1971

Literature: Alfred Robaut, *L'Oeuvre de Corot*, Paris: H. Floury, 1905, vol. III, p. 78, no. 1479, Robaut sketch p. 79

During the 1850s and 1860s Corot painted a number of views of the countryside to the southwest of Paris in the neighborhood of Sèvres and Ville-d'Avray. The Hammer picture is unusual among them for its broad panoramic composition and its precipitous movement from foreground to flat distant horizon without intervening transitional space. The intimate foreground stage which expands laterally without the usual large figure element (tree, house, etc.) is defined by the continuous vegetation parallel to the picture plane. In its more tangible depiction the foreground contrasts sharply with the almost impressionist horizon with its bare indications of architecture and the alternating ribbons of light and dark before it. These pictorial elements recall Phillips Koninck and Albert Cuyp and anticipate Monet. The color harmonies closely parallel the contemporary work of Boudin. The dome in the center distance is that of the Invalides; to the right are the towers of Nôtre Dame.

12 Camille Corot (1796-1875)
Morning
Oil on canvas: 69¹¹⁄₁₆" x 52⅜" (177.0 x 133.0 cm.)
Signed lower left: Corot

Collections: M. Larrieu, Bordeaux; E. Secrétan (Sale, July 1, 1889, no. 2)

Exhibitions: Paris, *Salon of 1865*, no. 506, under the title: *Le Matin*; Paris, Ecole des Beaux-Arts, 1875, no. 148 (lent by M. Larrieu, Bordeaux); Paris, Arnold & Tripp, Feb. 1883; Memphis, Tennessee, Brooks Memorial Art Gallery, *The Armand Hammer Collection*, Oct. 2-Dec. 30, 1969, no. 12 (repr. in cat.); Washington, D. C., Smithsonian Institution, *The Armand Hammer Collection*, Mar. 20-May 17, 1970, no. 12 (repr. in cat. in color); Smithsonian Institution Traveling Exhibition Service, *The Armand Hammer Collection*, Kansas City, Missouri, William Rockhill Nelson Gallery of Art, June 30-Aug. 2, 1970, New Orleans, Louisiana, Isaac Delgado Museum of Art, Aug. 15-Sept. 20, 1970, Columbus, Ohio, Columbus Gallery of Fine Arts, Oct. 9-Nov. 1, 1970, Little Rock, Arkansas, Arkansas Art Center, Nov. 21, 1970-Jan. 12, 1971; San Francisco, California, California Palace of the Legion of Honor, *The Armand Hammer Collection*, Feb. 11-Mar. 14, 1971; Oklahoma City, Oklahoma, Oklahoma Art Center, *The Armand Hammer Collection*, June 15-July 11, 1971

Literature: Alfred Robaut, *L'Art*, Paris, Feb. 18, 1883; Alfred Robaut, *L'Oeuvre de Corot*, Paris: H. Floury, 1905, vol. III, no. 1635, repr. p. 145; Etienne Moreau-Nélaton, *Corot, raconté par lui-même*, Paris: Henri Laurens, 1924, vol. II, fig. 191

Seeing this picture in the Salon of 1865 Paul Mantz wrote, "No landscape is as fresh, as tender, as bathed in the dawn as *Morning*," and in 1883 Alfred Robaut, decrying the small number of Corot paintings in French public collections, unsuccessfully demanded that the state allot one hundred thousand francs for its purchase. Robaut maintained that the composition had resulted from Corot's experience of an early morning in the country at Isigny and that a sketch made on the spot (Robaut 846) was preparatory to it. The sketch, however, bears only slight resemblance to the final composition. Of unusual importance because of its size, *Morning* combines Corot's favorite motifs of classical figures and a dark, but luminous setting seen against the light. The touch of red in the hair ribbon of the Bacchante is typical of him. The darkening of the picture in the century since it was painted somewhat obscures the original transparency of the coloring. The work has been known variously as *Morning*, *Bacchante*, and *Bacchante Detaining an Amoretto*.

13   Camille Corot (1796-1875)
     Pleasures of Evening
     Oil on canvas: 44½" x 65³/₁₆" (113.0 x 165.6 cm.)
     Signed and dated lower left: Corot 1875

Collections: Jay Gould, New York; Edwin J. Gould, New York

Exhibitions: Paris, *Salon of 1875*, no. 520; Paris, *Exposition Universelle Internationale de 1878*, no. 201; New York, American Art Galleries, *Exhibition of the Works of Antoine Barye and also Paintings by his Contemporaries and Friends, for the Benefit of the Barye Monument Fund*, Nov. 15, 1889-Jan. 15, 1890, no. 169 (lent by Jay Gould); New York, Hammer Galleries, *40th Anniversary Loan Exhibition, 1928-1968*, Nov. 7-Dec. 7, 1968 (repr. in cat. in color p. 18); Memphis, Tennessee, Brooks Memorial Art Gallery, *The Armand Hammer Collection*, Oct. 2-Dec. 30, 1969, no. 23 (repr. in cat.); Washington, D. C., Smithsonian Institution, *The Armand Hammer Collection*, Mar. 20-May 17, 1970, no. 24 (repr. in cat. in color); Smithsonian Institution Traveling Exhibition Service, *The Armand Hammer Collection*, Kansas City, Missouri, William Rockhill Nelson Gallery of Art, June 30-Aug. 2, 1970, New Orleans, Louisiana, Isaac Delgado Museum of Art, Aug. 15-Sept. 20, 1970, Columbus, Ohio, Columbus Gallery of Fine Arts, Oct. 9-Nov. 1, 1970, Little Rock, Arkansas, Arkansas Art Center, Nov. 21, 1970-Jan. 12, 1971; San Francisco, California, California Palace of the Legion of Honor, *The Armand Hammer Collection*, Feb. 11-Mar. 14, 1971; Oklahoma City, Oklahoma, Oklahoma Art Center, *The Armand Hammer Collection*, June 15-July 11, 1971

Literature: *Salon de 1875, 92ᵉ Exposition Officielle*, Paris: Imprimerie Nationale, 1875, p. 77, no. 520; A. de la Fizelière,

Memento du Salon de Peinture, de Gravure, et des Sculptures en 1875, Paris: Libraries des Bibliophiles, 1875, pp. 32, 65, no. 520; Paul Leroi, "Salon de 1875," *L'Art*, vol. II, XV, p. 269, repr. in lithograph; *L'Exposition de l'Oeuvre de Corot* (biographical note by P. Burty), Paris: 1875, p. 31; Anatole de Montaiglon, "Salon de 1875," *Gazettes des Beaux Arts*, 2nd series, vol. 12, p. 23; P. de la Flécherye, "Le Salon de 1875," *Le Monde*, Paris: Imprimerie Balitout, Questroy et Cie, 1875, p. 96; Henri Dumesnil, *Corot, Souvenirs Intimes*, Paris: Rapilly, 1875, pp. 102, 130, no. 120; *L'Alliance des Lettres et des Arts*, Apr. 1, 1875, repr. in pen drawing; *L'Univers Illustré*, May 1, 1875, repr. in woodcut; Jules Claretie, *L'Art et les Artistes Français Contemporains, Salon de 1875*, Paris: Charpentier et Cie., 1876, p. 356; *Catalogue Officiel de l'Exposition Universelle Internationale de 1878 à Paris*, Paris: Imprimerie Nationale, 1878, vol. I, section I (Oeuvres d'Art), p. 20, no. 201; *Exposition Universelle Internationale de Paris, 1878, Le Livre d'Or des Exposants*, Paris: André Sagnier, 1878, p. 8; Paul Mantz, "L'Art Moderne à l'Exposition de 1878, La Peinture Française," *Gazette des Beaux Arts*, Paris: A. Quantin, 1879, p. 24; Jules Claretie, "C. Corot," *Peintres et Sculpteurs Contemporains*, 1st series, Paris, 1882, pp. 97-120; J. Castagnary, *Salons, 1857-1879*, Paris: Charpentier et Cie, 1892, vol. II, p. 41; *Corot and Millet, with Critical Essays by Gustave Geffroy and Arsène Alexandre*, London and New York: Offices of *The Studio*, 1902, p. CXXVIII; Etienne Moreau-Nélaton, *Histoire de Corot et de Ses Oeuvres*, Paris: H. Floury, 1905, fig. 260, pp. 342, 359; Alfred Robaut, *L'Oeuvre de Corot*, Paris: H. Floury, 1905, vol. I, p. 333, vol. III, pp. 322-323, no. 2195, repr., vol. IV, pp. 170, 278, 378, table p. 34; Etienne Moreau-Nélaton, *Corot, raconté par lui-même*, Paris: Henri Laurens, 1924, fig. 258, pp. 89, 105, repr. p. 175; Germain Bazin, *Corot*, Paris: Editions Pierre Tisné, 1951 (2nd ed.), p. 115; Daniel Band-Bovy, *Corot*, Geneva: Alexandre Julien, 1957, p. 251; *Apollo*, May 1967, p. LXXIV, repr.

Castagnary wrote of this picture and the *Woodcutters*, both exhibited posthumously in the Salon of 1875, that they were "worthy of the most beautiful among their predecessors." Among the last of Corot's paintings, *Pleasures of Evening* repeats the theme of an antique dance in the forest that he had treated more than once before. Begun at Courbron, a small town just east of Paris where Corot was in the habit of visiting friends and working toward the end of his life, the picture was finished in Paris. Between its inception and its completion it was sketched by Robaut (2195 [A]). It is clear from the sketch that Corot made several changes after his return to Paris, apparently reworking the figures in the group at right center and adding the two figures at the left.

14 Eugène Boudin (1824-1898)
Sailing Ships in Port
Oil on canvas: 17¾" x 25⁵/₁₆" (45.1 x 64.3 cm.)
Signed and dated lower left: E. Boudin 1869

Collection: Allard et Noël, Paris

Exhibitions: New York, Hammer Galleries, *40th Anniversary Loan Exhibition 1928-1968*, Nov. 7-Dec. 7, 1968 (repr. in color p. 15); Memphis, Tennessee, Brooks Memorial Art Gallery, *The Armand Hammer Collection*, Oct. 2-Dec. 30, 1969, no. 26 (repr. in cat.); Washington, D. C., Smithsonian Institution, *The Armand Hammer Collection*, Mar. 20-May 17, 1970, no. 27 (repr. in cat. in color); Smithsonian Institution Traveling Exhibition Service, *The Armand Hammer Collection*, Kansas City, Missouri, William Rockhill Nelson Gallery of Art, June 30-Aug. 2, 1970, New Orleans, Louisiana, Isaac Delgado Museum of Art, Aug. 15-Sept. 20, 1970, Columbus, Ohio, Columbus Gallery of Fine Arts, Oct. 9-Nov. 1, 1970, Little Rock, Arkansas, Arkansas Art Center, Nov. 21, 1970-Jan. 12, 1971; San Francisco, California, California Palace of the Legion of Honor, *The Armand Hammer Collection*, Feb. 11-Mar. 14, 1971; Oklahoma City, Oklahoma, Oklahoma Art Center, *The Armand Hammer Collection*, June 15-July 11, 1971; San Diego, California, Fine Arts Gallery of San Diego, *The Armand Hammer Collection*, July 23-Sept. 5, 1971

Descended from seventeenth-century Holland by way of eighteenth-century Venetian *vedute*, Boudin's paintings contrast towering, broadly-brushed skies with more precisely-rendered, flickering groups of figures, ships, and buildings stretched out along the horizon. The precision of their naturalistic observation and their narrow tonal range of grayed blue, green, and ochre sparked with occasional accents of red attracted the attention of the young Impressionists, most notably that of Monet. In 1869, the year of this picture, Boudin wrote of "the sundrenched beaches and the stormy skies, and of the joy of painting them in the sea breezes."

15 Eugène Boudin (1824-1898)
Quay at Camaret
Oil on canvas: 14½" x 23" (36.8 x 58.4 cm.)
Signed and dated lower left: Boudin '73
Inscribed lower right: Camaret

Collections: Bernheim-Jeune, Paris; L. Bernard; Théodore Révillon, Paris; Georges Petit, Paris; Galerie Schmit, Paris

Exhibitions: New York, Hammer Galleries, *40th Anniversary Loan Exhibition, 1928-1968*, Nov. 7-Dec. 7, 1968 (repr. in color p. 14); Memphis, Tennessee, Brooks Memorial Art Gallery, *The Armand Hammer Collection*, Oct. 2-Dec. 30, 1969, no. 27 (repr. in cat.); Washington, D. C., Smithsonian

Institution, *The Armand Hammer Collection*, Mar. 20-May 17, 1970, no. 28 (repr. in cat. in color); Smithsonian Institution Traveling Exhibition Service, *The Armand Hammer Collection*, Kansas City, Missouri, William Rockhill Nelson Gallery of Art, June 30-Aug. 2, 1970, New Orleans, Louisiana, Isaac Delgado Museum of Art, Aug. 15-Sept. 20, 1970, Columbus, Ohio, Columbus Gallery of Fine Arts, Oct. 9-Nov. 1, 1970, Little Rock, Arkansas, Arkansas Art Center, Nov. 21, 1970-Jan. 12, 1971; San Francisco, California, California Palace of the Legion of Honor, *The Armand Hammer Collection*, Feb. 11-Mar. 14, 1971; Oklahoma City, Oklahoma, Oklahoma Art Center, *The Armand Hammer Collection*, June 15-July 11, 1971; San Diego, California, Fine Arts Gallery of San Diego, *The Armand Hammer Collection*, July 23-Sept. 5, 1971

In 1872 and 1873 Boudin worked at Camaret, at the extreme western tip of Brittany. This picture, somewhat stronger in its tonal contrasts than is common for him, seems almost an illustration of Gustave Geffroy's statement that "Eugène Boudin is one of the immediate precursors of Impressionism . . . . He has perceived that opaque black does not exist, and that air is transparent. He observes the value that objects acquire when exposed to light, and how planes fall into place and lead to the horizon." Boudin himself, constantly conscious of the gap between his perceptions and his expressive powers, wrote, "Sometimes, as I walk sunken in melancholy, I look at the light inundating the earth, trembling on the water, playing on clothing, and I become faint when I realize how much genius is needed to grasp so many difficulties."

16 Eugène Boudin (1824-1898)
Beach at Trouville
Oil on canvas: 12⅞" x 7⁵/₁₆" (32.7 x 18.6 cm.)
Signed lower right: a Mⁿˢ Sonnerville (sic)
Souvenir de E. Boudin
Inscribed lower left: Trouville

Collections: de Sonneville, Bordeaux; Hallsborough, London; Lock Galleries, New York

Exhibitions: New York, Hammer Galleries, *40th Anniversary Loan Exhibition 1928-1968*, Nov. 7-Dec. 7, 1968 (repr. in color p. 12); Memphis, Tennessee, Brooks Memorial Art Gallery, *The Armand Hammer Collection*, Oct. 2-Dec. 30, 1969, no. 28 (repr. in cat.); Washington, D. C., Smithsonian Institution, *The Armand Hammer Collection*, Mar. 20-May 17, 1970, no. 29 (repr. in cat. in color); Smithsonian Institution Traveling Exhibition Service, *The Armand Hammer Collection*, Kansas City, Missouri, William Rockhill Nelson Gallery of Art, June 30-Aug. 2, 1970, New Orleans, Louisiana, Isaac Delgado Museum of Art, Aug. 15-Sept. 20, 1970, Columbus, Ohio, Columbus Gallery of Fine Arts, Oct. 9-Nov. 1, 1970, Little Rock, Arkansas, Arkansas Art Center, Nov. 21, 1970-Jan. 12, 1971; San Francisco,

California, California Palace of the Legion of Honor, *The Armand Hammer Collection*, Feb. 11-Mar. 14, 1971; Oklahoma City, Oklahoma, Oklahoma Art Center, *The Armand Hammer Collection*, June 15-July 11, 1971; San Diego, California, Fine Arts Gallery of San Diego, *The Armand Hammer Collection*, July 23-Sept. 5, 1971

Literature: *Art News*, Feb. 1967, repr. p. 53

The horizontal format of this sketch and its frieze-like arrangement of people midway in the composition are characteristic of Boudin's beach scenes. This one was taken at Trouville, one of his favorite haunts and among the most fashionable of the Second Empire resorts.

17 Gustave Caillebotte (1848-1894)
Square in Argenteuil
Oil on canvas: 23¹³/₁₆" x 27¾" (60.5 x 70.5 cm.)
Signed lower left: G. Caillebotte

Exhibitions: Smithsonian Institution Traveling Exhibition Service, *The Armand Hammer Collection*, New Orleans, Louisiana, Isaac Delgado Museum of Art, Aug. 15-Sept. 20, 1970, Columbus, Ohio, Columbus Gallery of Fine Arts, Oct. 9-Nov. 1, 1970, Little Rock, Arkansas, Arkansas Art Center, Nov. 21, 1970-Jan. 12, 1971; San Francisco, California, California Palace of the Legion of Honor, *The Armand Hammer Collection*, Feb. 11-Mar. 14, 1971; Oklahoma City, Oklahoma, Oklahoma Art Center, *The Armand Hammer Collection*, June 15-July 11, 1971; San Diego, California, Fine Arts Gallery of San Diego, *The Armand Hammer Collection*, July 23-Sept. 5, 1971

Literature: Sale catalog, *Importants Tableaux Modernes*, Paris: Palais Galliéra, June 17, 1970, no. 9

Known principally as the collector who bequeathed the first great group of Impressionist pictures to the French state, Caillebotte was among the organizers of, and participants in, many of the original Impressionist exhibitions. As a painter, his vision was almost always advanced, and he favored subjects from daily life in natural poses although his execution was often tight and linear to the point of academicism. Caillebotte was at his best in his broadly conceived and freely brushed canvases many of which, like this one, were executed at Argenteuil. This fresh and unexpected work probably dates from the early 1880s.

18 Alfred Sisley (1839-1899)
Timber Yard at Saint-Mammès, 1880
Oil on canvas: 21½" x 28¾" (55.6 x 72.9 cm.)
Signed lower right: Sisley

Collections: M. Feder, Paris; Durand-Ruel, Paris (purchased June 25, 1892); Paul Cassirer, Berlin; Galerie Europe, Brussels; Sale, London, Sotheby & Co., Nov. 29, 1967, no. 28, repr. p. 46

Exhibitions: Paris, Galerie Durand-Ruel, *Monet, Pissarro, Renoir et Sisley*, Apr. 1899, no. 136; London, Grafton Gallery, *Paintings by Boudin, Sisley*, Jan.-Feb. 1905, no. 303; Paris, Galerie Durand-Ruel, *Sisley*, June 1910, no. 71; New York, Hammer Galleries, *40th Anniversary Loan Exhibition 1928-1968*, Nov. 7-Dec. 7, 1968 (repr. color in cat. p. 52); Memphis, Tennessee, Brooks Memorial Art Gallery, *The Armand Hammer Collection*, Oct. 2-Dec. 30, 1969, no. 37 (repr. in cat.); Washington, D. C., Smithsonian Institution, *The Armand Hammer Collection*, Mar. 20-May 17, 1970, no. 40 (repr. in cat. in color); Smithsonian Institution Traveling Exhibition Service, *The Armand Hammer Collection*, Kansas City, Missouri, William Rockhill Nelson Gallery of Art, June 30-Aug 2, 1970, New Orleans, Louisiana, Isaac Delgado Museum of Art, Aug. 15-Sept. 20, 1970, Columbus, Ohio, Columbus Gallery of Fine Arts, Oct. 9-Nov. 1,,1970, Little Rock, Arkansas, Arkansas Art Center, Nov. 21, 1970-Jan. 12, 1971; San Francisco, California, California Palace of the Legion of Honor, *The Armand Hammer Collection*, Feb. 11-Mar. 14, 1971; Oklahoma City, Oklahoma, Oklahoma Art Center, *The Armand Hammer Collection*, June 15-July 11, 1971; San Diego, California, Fine Arts Gallery of San Diego, *The Armand Hammer Collection*, July 23-Sept. 5, 1971

Literature: Gustave Geffroy, *Sisley*, Paris: G. Crès et Cie., 1923, repr. pl. 10; Gustave Geffroy, *Cahiers d'Aujourd'hui*, Paris, 1923, vols. 13, 14, pp. 7-30; Gustave Geffroy, *Sisley*, Paris: G. Crès et Cie., 1927, repr. pl. 28; Gotthard Jedlicka, *Sisley*, Bern, 1949, repr. pl. 37; François Daulte, *Alfred Sisley, Catalogue Raisonné de l'Oeuvre Peint*, Lausanne: Durand-Ruel, 1959, no. 368, repr. p. 372; Sale catalog, *Impressionist and Modern Paintings, Drawings and Sculpture*, London: Sotheby & Co., Nov. 29, 1967, p. 47, no. 28, repr. color p. 46; *Burlington Magazine*, Nov. 1967, p. 1 repr.; *Apollo*, Nov. 1967, p. CXVIII, repr.; *Art News*, Nov. 1967, p. 17, repr.; *Apollo*, June 1968, p. CII, repr.; *Connoisseur*, June 1968, p. XIV, repr.

Sisley was at his best in broad, close-valued, tonal painting. The typical comma-like Impressionist facture tended to be disruptive of such painting, and Sisley used it most effectively when his strokes were of fairly uniform size and shape and his colors within one or two narrow ranges of tone, as in this picture. Saint-Mammès, to which Sisley eventually retired, was a small town on the banks of the Loing in the area southeast of Fontainebleau. Daulte lists at least three other compositions directly related to this (369, 370, 372) and one of the same scene from the opposite direction (371).

19 Claude Monet (1840-1926)
View of Bordighera
Oil on canvas: 26" x 32¼" (66.0 x 81.9 cm.)
Signed and dated lower left: Claude Monet '84

Collections: Durand-Ruel, Paris; M. Montaignac, Paris; James F. Sutton, New York (Sale, American Art Association at the Plaza Hotel, Jan. 16-17, 1917, no. 143); James B. Hastings, New York; Nils B. Hersloff, Baltimore; Estate of Sigmund N. Hersloff, Baltimore (Sale, New York, Parke-Bernet Galleries, Inc., Oct. 28, 1970, no. 5, p. 8, repr. in color)

Exhibitions: Paris, Galerie Georges Petit, *Claude Monet et A. Rodin*, 1889 (lent by M. Montaignac); Smithsonian Institution Traveling Exhibition Service, *The Armand Hammer Collection*, Little Rock, Arkansas, Arkansas Art Center, Nov. 21, 1970-Jan. 12, 1971; San Francisco, California, California Palace of the Legion of Honor, *The Armand Hammer Collection*, Feb. 11-Mar. 14, 1971; Oklahoma City, Oklahoma, Oklahoma Art Center, *The Armand Hammer Collection*, June 15-July 11, 1971; San Diego, California, Fine Arts Gallery of San Diego, *The Armand Hammer Collection*, July 23-Sept. 5, 1971

Literature: Theodore Robinson, "Monet," *Modern French Masters, A Series of Biographical and Critical Reviews by American Artists, with 37 Wood Engravings and 28 Half-Tone Illustrations*, by John Charles Van Dyke, wood engraving by Michael Haider, New York: The Century Co., 1896, p. 170; *Apollo*, Oct. 1970, p. 141, repr.; *Burlington Magazine*, Oct. 1970, LXXIV, repr.; *Art News*, Oct. 1970, repr.

During the 1880s Monet's palette darkened, a fact which, combined with the discreteness and small size of his brushstrokes and the intensity and value contrasts of his color, tended to give his pictures a woolly texture that is especially noticeable in the Creuse and Belle-Ile paintings. This picture contrasts that roughness with an atmospheric distance and is therefore somewhat less surface-oriented than the similar painting in Chicago. Monet had been attracted to the south on a visit there with Renior in 1883, and in January of 1884 he returned to paint first at Bordighera, on the Italian Riviera, and then at Menton.

20   Pierre Auguste Renoir (1841-1919)
Two Girls Reading, 1890-1891
Oil on canvas: 22" x 18⅝" (55.9 x 47.2 cm.)
Signed lower right: Renoir

Collections: Durand-Ruel, Paris (purchased from Renoir in 1895); H. O. Niethke Gallery, Vienna (purchased 1912); Dr. Herman Eissler, Vienna; Hugo Moser, Heemstede; Mrs. Maria Moser, New York; Dr. and Mrs. Armand Hammer, Los Angeles; Los Angeles County Museum of Art (Gift of Dr. and Mrs. Armand Hammer, 1968)

Exhibitions: Zurich, Kunsthaus, 1933; Haarlem, Frans Hals Museum, 1936; Baltimore Museum of Art, Summer 1939; New York, Wildenstein & Co., Inc., *Renoir*, Apr. 8-May 10, 1958, no. 53, p. 67 (repr. in cat.); New York, The Metropolitan Museum of Art, 1959-1967; New York, Hammer Galleries, *40th Anniversary Loan Exhibition 1928-1968*, Nov. 7-Dec. 7, 1968 (repr. in color in cat. p. 47); New York, Wildenstein & Co., Inc., *Renoir*, Mar. 27-May 3, 1969, no. 77 (repr. in cat.); Memphis, Tennessee, Brooks Memorial Art Gallery, *The Armand Hammer Collection*, Oct. 2-Dec. 30, 1969, no. 44 (repr. in cat.); Washington, D. C., Smithsonian Institution, *The Armand Hammer Collection*, Mar. 20-May 17, 1970, no. 51 (repr. in cat. in color); Smithsonian Institution Traveling Exhibition Service, *The Armand Hammer Collection*, New Orleans, Louisiana, Isaac Delgado Museum of Art, Aug. 15-Sept. 20, 1970; San Francisco, California, California Palace of the Legion of Honor, *The Armand Hammer Collection*, Feb. 11-Mar. 14, 1971; San Diego, California, Fine Arts Gallery of San Diego, *The Armand Hammer Collection*, July 23-Sept. 5, 1971

Literature: Baltimore Museum of Art *Quarterly*, July 1, 1939, p. 8, repr.; Los Angeles County Museum of Art *Annual Report*, 1968-1969, pp. 18-19, repr.; Alfred Weiner, "Renoir's Daimon," *Arts Magazine*, Apr. 1969, p. 40, repr.; *Gazette des Beaux-Arts*, Feb. 1970, supplement, p. 87, repr.

This gentle and slightly nostalgic subject is of the kind that most appealed to Renoir and that he was best able to execute successfully. The consistency of the brushwork and warmth of the color help unify the composition, and the painting shows the renewed softness of Renoir's work toward the end of the century. The girl at the left is said to be Julie Manet, daughter of Berthe Morisot and Eugène Manet, while the one at the right is possibly her cousin Paule Gobillard. A less satisfying variation of this composition is recorded in a Scottish private collection (reproduced *Scottish Art Review*, vol. IV, no. 4, 1953, p. 19), and there is also a three-quarter length variation of a similar subject (reproduced *Beaux-Arts*, Feb. 22, 1935, p. 4).

21   Pierre Auguste Renoir (1841-1919)
Antibes
Oil on canvas: 25½" x 32" (64.8 x 81.3 cm.)
Signed and dated lower right: Renoir '88

Collections: Durand-Ruel, Paris, 1910; Baroness von Brenin, Berlin, 1931; Sale, New York, Parke-Bernet Galleries, Inc., Feb. 25, 1970, no. 21 (repr.)

Exhibitions: Paris, Durand-Ruel, *Exposition de Tableaux par Renoir*, Apr. 27-May 15, 1912, no. 5; Akron, Ohio, Akron Art Institute, 1947; Milwaukee, Wisconsin, Milwaukee Art Institute, *Masters of Impressionism*, 1948, no. 38; Smithsonian Institution Traveling Exhibition Service, *The Armand Hammer Collection*, Kansas City, Missouri, William Rockhill Nelson Gallery of Art, June 30-Aug. 2, 1970, New Orleans, Louisiana, Isaac Delgado Museum of Art, Aug. 15-Sept. 20, 1970, Columbus, Ohio, Columbus Gallery of Fine Arts, Oct. 9-Nov. 1, 1970, Little Rock,

Arkansas, Arkansas Art Center, Nov. 21, 1970-Jan. 12, 1971, no. 100 (repr. in cat. supplement); San Francisco, California, California Palace of the Legion of Honor, *The Armand Hammer Collection*, Feb. 11-Mar. 14, 1971; Oklahoma City, Oklahoma, Oklahoma Art Center, *The Armand Hammer Collection*, June 15-July 11, 1971; San Diego, California, Fine Arts Gallery of San Diego, *The Armand Hammer Collection*, July 23-Sept. 5, 1971

Literature: Sale catalog, *Highly Important Impressionist, Post-Impressionist & Modern Paintings and Drawings*, New York: Parke-Bernet Galleries, Inc., Feb. 25, 1970, no. 21, repr. in color

During the 1880s Renoir's efforts to re-study his draftsmanship resulted in a hard and carefully-outlined figure style usually at variance with the continued softness of his backgrounds. Only in the non-figural subjects, such as this view of Antibes, did he maintain and develop his feathery brush style, suppressing contour to an extent which makes the subjects of these pictures seem almost to evaporate. A similar composition is recorded in the collection of Sir Simon and Lady Marks.

22 Pierre Auguste Renoir (1841-1919)
Grape Pickers at Lunch, ca. 1888
Oil on canvas: 21⅞″ x 18¼″ (55.5 x 46.4 cm.)
Signed lower left: Renoir

Collections: Arsène Alexandre, Paris; Rosenberg & Stiebel, New York

Exhibitions: Memphis, Tennessee, Brooks Memorial Art Gallery, *The Armand Hammer Collection*, Oct. 2-Dec. 30, 1969, no. 43 (repr. in cat.); Washington, D. C., Smithsonian Institution, *The Armand Hammer Collection*, Mar. 20-May 17, 1970, no. 50 (repr. in cat. in color); Smithsonian Institution Traveling Exhibition Service, *The Armand Hammer Collection*, Kansas City, Missouri, William Rockhill Nelson Gallery of Art, June 30-Aug. 2, 1970, New Orleans, Louisiana, Isaac Delgado Museum of Art, Aug. 15-Sept. 20, 1970, Columbus, Ohio, Columbus Gallery of Fine Arts, Oct. 9-Nov. 1, 1970, Little Rock, Arkansas, Arkansas Art Center, Nov. 21, 1970-Jan. 12, 1971; San Francisco, California, California Palace of the Legion of Honor, *The Armand Hammer Collection*, Feb. 11-Mar. 14, 1971; Oklahoma City, Oklahoma Art Center, *The Armand Hammer Collection*, June 15-July 11, 1971

Literature: Sale catalog, Paris: Galerie Georges Petit, May 1903, no. 54

This picture, with its sharp contrasts of hue and its carefully drawn forms, is a product of the mid-1880s—a period of experimentation and re-evaluation for Renoir. He had earlier questioned the validity of recording purely visual impressions, and after studying the Raphael paintings in Rome and the ancient frescoes from Pompeii in the Naples

Museum during an Italian trip in 1881-1882, Renoir sought to reassess the importance of drawing, line, modeled form, and compositional reorganization of nature. He even questioned the soundness of painting in the open air directly from nature as opposed to composing in the studio. Like Cézanne, but in his own way, he devoted himself at this time to establishing harmony between Impressionism and the "art of the museums."

The *Grape Pickers at Lunch* is a product of Renoir's exploration of some of these concepts. Instead of his usual soft brushwork, he uses smaller, sharper, more graphic strokes which define and model the figures. Instead of merging his figures with the landscape, as in the Impressionist works of the seventies, he arranges his figures to form a closed concentric group which establishes a real, but limited foreground space, reminiscent of Renaissance "stage-like" space, to which the landscape forms a backdrop.

The probability that the painting is a studio composition is reinforced by the reappearance of the girl with the basket on her back used by Renoir in the *Mussel Gatherers at Berneval*, painted in 1879 and shown in the Salon of 1880. The three girls in the foreground are said to be the daughters of Paul Alexis.

23 Camille Pissarro (1830-1903)
Boulevard Montmartre, Mardi Gras
Oil on canvas: 25″ x 31½″ (63.5 x 77.5 cm.)
Signed and dated lower left: C. Pissarro '97

Collections: Maurice Barret-Décap, Paris; Mr. and Mrs. Henry R. Luce, New York; Marlborough Alte und Moderne Kunst, Zurich; Norton Simon, Los Angeles (Sale, New York, Parke-Bernet Galleries, May 5, 1971, no. 24, repr.)

Exhibitions: Paris, Galerie Durand-Ruel, *C. Pissarro*, 1898, no. 20; Paris, Galerie Durand-Ruel, *Tableaux, Pastels et Gouaches de C. Pissarro*, 1921, no. 9; Paris, Galerie Durand-Ruel, *C. Pissarro*, 1928, no. 78; New Haven, Yale University Art Gallery, *Paintings, Drawings, and Sculpture Collected by Yale Alumni*, May 19-June 26, 1960, no. 58 (repr. in cat.); New York, Wildenstein & Co., Inc., *C. Pissarro*, Mar. 25-May 1, 1965, no. 65, (repr. in cat.); Oklahoma City, Oklahoma, Oklahoma Art Center, *The Armand Hammer Collection*, June 15-July 11, 1971; San Diego, California, Fine Arts Gallery of San Diego, *The Armand Hammer Collection*, July 23-Sept. 5, 1971

Literature: Ludovic-Rodo Pissarro and Lionello Venturi, *C. Pissarro, Son Art—Son Oeuvre*, 1939, no. 995, repr., vol. II, pl. 200; Sale catalog, *Highly Important 19th and 20th Century Paintings, Drawings and Sculpture from the Private Collection of Norton Simon*, New York: Parke-Bernet Galleries, May 5, 1971, no. 24, p. 40, repr. opp. in color

Pissarro produced several paintings of the Boulevard

Montmartre in 1897 (Venturi-Pissarro 986-998), three of which (Venturi-Pissarro 995-997) seem to represent successive stages of a Lenten parade. Although the three are surely related, two, including this one, are catalogued by Venturi and Pissarro as Mardi Gras scenes and the third as a Mi-Carême. This picture is characteristic of Pissarro's late interest in city scenes, particularly views of Paris, seen at sharp downward angles. Characteristic too are the blond tonality and obvious feathery or calligraphic brushwork he used toward the end of his life. Partly because of the nature of the subject, this picture has somewhat more color than others of Pissarro's Paris views.

24 Henri Fantin-Latour (1836-1904)
Peonies in a Blue and White Vase
Oil on canvas: 23 15/16″ x 19⅝″ (60.8 x 49.9 cm.)
Signed and dated upper right: Fantin 1872

Collections: Dr. J. van Alphen-Carp, The Netherlands; E. J. van Wisselingh & Co., Amsterdam; M. L. de Boer, Amsterdam

Exhibitions: New York, Hammer Galleries, *40th Anniversary Loan Exhibition, 1928-1968*, Nov. 7-Dec. 7, 1968 (repr. in cat. in color p. 28); Memphis, Tennessee, Brooks Memorial Art Gallery, *The Armand Hammer Collection*, Oct. 2-Dec. 30, 1969, no. 34 (repr. in cat.); Washington, D. C., Smithsonian Institution, *The Armand Hammer Collection*, Mar. 20-May 17, 1970, no. 36 (repr. in cat. in color); Smithsonian Institution Traveling Exhibition Service, *The Armand Hammer Collection*, Kansas City, Missouri, William Rockhill Nelson Gallery of Art, June 30-Aug. 2, 1970, New Orleans, Louisiana, Isaac Delgado Museum of Art, Aug. 15-Sept. 20, 1970, Columbus, Ohio, Columbus Gallery of Fine Arts, Oct. 9-Nov. 1, 1970, Little Rock, Arkansas, Arkansas Art Center, Nov. 21, 1970-Jan. 12, 1971; San Francisco, California, California Palace of the Legion of Honor, *The Armand Hammer Collection*, Feb. 11-Mar. 14, 1971; Oklahoma City, Oklahoma, Oklahoma Art Center, *The Armand Hammer Collection*, June 15-July 11, 1971; San Diego, California, Fine Arts Gallery of San Diego, *The Armand Hammer Collection*, July 23-Sept. 5, 1971

Literature: Mme. Fantin-Latour, *Catalogue de l'Oevure Complet de Fantin-Latour*, Paris: H. Floury, 1911, no. 616; *Art Journal*, Fall 1968, p. LIV, repr.; *Connoisseur*, Nov. 1968, p. 11, repr.; François Daulte, "Hammer en dix chefs-d'oeuvre," *Connaissance des Arts*, Sept. 1970, p. 83, repr.

Fantin is most widely known for his flower pictures, in the best of which white predominates against a cool-hued background. Seen in isolation, the flowers in these paintings project in astonishing relief and tactility. This heightened sense of reality is partly due to the apparent lack of atmosphere in the flower pieces. Perhaps none of these paintings illustrates as well as this one Jacques-Emile

Blanche's observation that "Fantin studied each flower, each petal, its grain, its tissue as if it were a human face . . . It is an individual flower and not simply one of a type . . . . Some canvases are worthy of Chardin."

25 Henri Fantin-Latour (1836-1904)
Portrait of Miss Edith Crowe
Oil on canvas: 28¾″ x 23⁵/₁₆″ (73.0 x 59.2 cm.)
Signed and dated upper left: Fantin '74

Collections: Mme. Paul Paix; Mrs. D. Bergen-Hayn; Galerie l'Oeil, Paris

Exhibitions: Paris, *Salon of 1875*, no. 783; Paris, Ecole Nationale des Beaux-Arts, *Exposition de l'Oeuvre de Fantin-Latour*, May-June 1906, no. 41; Amsterdam, Stedelijk Museum; Memphis, Tennessee, Brooks Memorial Art Gallery, *The Armand Hammer Collection*, Oct. 2-Dec. 30, 1969, no. 35 (repr.); Washington, D. C., Smithsonian Institution, *The Armand Hammer Collection*, Mar. 20-May 17, 1970, no. 37 (repr. in cat. in color); Smithsonian Institution Traveling Exhibition Service, *The Armand Hammer Collection*, Kansas City, Missouri, William Rockhill Nelson Gallery of Art, June 30-Aug. 2, 1970, New Orleans, Louisiana, Isaac Delgado Museum of Art, Aug. 15-Sept. 20, 1970, Columbus, Ohio, Columbus Gallery of Fine Arts, Oct. 9-Nov. 1, 1970, Little Rock, Arkansas, Arkansas Art Center, Nov. 21, 1970-Jan. 12, 1971; San Francisco, California, California Palace of the Legion of Honor, *The Armand Hammer Collection*, Feb. 11-Mar. 14, 1971; Oklahoma City, Oklahoma, Oklahoma Art Center, *The Armand Hammer Collection*, June 15-July 11, 1971

Literature: Ministère de l'Instruction Publique et des Beaux-Arts, *Salon de 1875, 92ᵉᵐᵉ Exposition Officielle*, Paris: Imprimerie Nationale, 1875, p. 115, no. 783; Paul Leroi, *L'Art, Salon de 1875*, Paris: Librairie de l'Art, 1875, vol. I, p. 137, no. 783; Adolphe Julien, *Fantin-Latour, sa vie et ses amitiés*, Paris: Lucien Laveur, 1909, p. 199; Mme. Fantin-Latour, *Catalogue de l'oeuvre complet de Fantin-Latour*, Paris: H. Floury, 1911, p. 81, no. 739; *Connoisseur*, Nov. 1970, p. 210, repr.

This picture was exhibited as "Portrait of Mlle. E. C.***" in the Salon of 1875 along with Fantin's superb double portrait of his English friends and patrons Mr. and Mrs. Edwin Edwards, to whom he had been introduced by Whistler. Miss Crowe was presumably a friend of the Edwards', or of someone to whom Fantin had been introduced by them. Broader in technique than Fantin's flower pieces, this picture is not yet as free as the allegories and Wagnerian paintings which are almost pre-Raphaelite in character. The placement of the figure against an unmodulated dark ground suggests what Fantin may owe to Manet, although the head is developed in a more traditional chiaroscuro. Speaking of another of Fantin's portraits, Zola noted that "Each of his canvases is an act of conscience. He excels at painting figures in the atmosphere in which they live, in giving them a warm and supple life; it is that which means that, despite the restraining frame in which it is enclosed, this hardly seems to be a portrait, it is nothing less than a thing apart, very elevated."

26 Henri Fantin-Latour (1836-1904)
Roses
Oil on canvas: 26 1/16" x 22 11/16" (66.2 x 57.7 cm.)
Signed and dated upper left: Fantin '84

Collections: Mrs. Edwards, London; Miss R. Bryant, London; Arthur Tooth & Sons, Ltd., London; Mrs. Hazel C. Boise, London (Sale, London, Sotheby & Co., Apr. 26, 1967, no. 7, repr. p. 14)

Exhibitions: Musée de Grenoble, *Exposition du Centenaire de la Naissance de Fantin-Latour*, Aug.-Oct. 1936, no. 145; London, Arthur Tooth & Sons, Ltd., *French Pictures from Private Collections*, June 1949, no. 19; New York, Hammer Galleries, *40th Anniversary Loan Exhibition, 1928-1968*, Nov. 7-Dec. 7, 1968 (repr. in cat. in color p. 27); Memphis, Tennessee, Brooks Memorial Art Gallery, *The Armand Hammer Collection*, Oct. 2-Dec. 30, 1969, no. 36 (repr. in cat.); Washington, D. C., Smithsonian Institution, *The Armand Hammer Collection*, Mar. 20-May 17, 1970, no. 38 (repr. in cat. in color); Smithsonian Institution Traveling Exhibition Service, *The Armand Hammer Collection*, Kansas City, Missouri, William Rockhill Nelson Gallery of Art, June 30-Aug. 2, 1970, New Orleans, Louisiana, Isaac Delgado Museum of Art, Aug. 15-Sept. 20, 1970, Columbus, Ohio, Columbus Gallery of Fine Arts, Oct. 9-Nov. 1, 1970, Little Rock, Arkansas, Arkansas Art Center, Nov. 21, 1970-Jan. 12, 1971; San Francisco, California, California Palace of the Legion of Honor, *The Armand Hammer Collection*, Feb. 11-Mar. 14, 1971; Oklahoma City, Oklahoma, Oklahoma Art Center, *The Armand Hammer Collection*, June 15-July 11, 1971; San Diego, California, Fine Arts Gallery of San Diego, *The Armand Hammer Collection*, July 23-Sept. 5, 1971

Literature: Mme. Fantin-Latour, *Catalogue de l'Oeuvre Complet de Fantin-Latour*, Paris: H. Floury, 1911, no. 1167; *Burlington Magazine*, Apr. 1967, p. XVI, repr.; *Connoisseur*, Apr. 1967, p. XCIII, repr.; Sale catalog, *Impressionist and Modern Paintings and Sculpture*, London: Sotheby & Co., Apr. 1967, p. 15, no. 7, repr. p. 14

The Mrs. Edwards who originally owned this picture is presumably Mrs. Edwin Edwards, wife of Fantin's English friend and patron. Although Fantin's portraits and genre subjects were favored in France, his flower pictures were particularly popular in England, and his submissions to the Royal Academy between 1862 and 1900 consisted almost entirely of such subjects. Many of these had poetic titles

such as, "Here Without a Thorn, the Rose." Although this picture seems originally to have been called simply *Roses*, it has been known as *All the Roses of the Garden*, probably because of Madame Fantin-Latour's description of it in her catalog. *Roses* is a "poetic," close-valued, and somewhat more broadly-brushed painting than the Hammer *Peonies*, the pastel pinks and yellows mediating between the white highlights and the deep red and green darks to soften the picture's general appearance. This atmospheric facture is particularly appropriate in view of the literary associations roses seem regularly to have evoked in Fantin.

27 Edgar Degas (1834-1917)
Three Dancers in Yellow Skirts, ca. 1891
Oil on canvas: 32" x 25⅝" (81.3 x 65.1 cm.)
Signed lower right: Degas

Collections: Atelier Degas (1st Sale, Paris, Galerie Georges Petit, May 6-8, 1918, no. 82, repr.); MM. Nunès and Fiquet, Paris; F. R. (Sale, Paris, Mar. 8, 1930, no. 74); Galerie René Drouet, Paris; Erwin Swann, Pennsylvania (Sale, London, Sotheby & Co., Dec. 10, 1969, no. 20, repr.)

Exhibitions: New York, Gallery of Modern Art, *The Pleasure of the Eye—The Collection of Caroline and Erwin Swann*, 1964-65, no. 9; Portland Art Museum; Seattle Art Museum; Salt Lake Art Center; Colorado Springs Fine Arts Center; Kansas City, William Rockhill Nelson Gallery of Art; University of Michigan, Museum of Art; Dayton Art Institute; Washington, D. C., Smithsonian Institution, *The Armand Hammer Collection*, Mar. 20-May 17, 1970, no. 34 (repr. in cat. in color); Smithsonian Institution Traveling Exhibition Service, *The Armand Hammer Collection*, Kansas City, Missouri, William Rockhill Nelson Gallery of Art, June 30-Aug. 2, 1970, New Orleans, Louisiana, Isaac Delgado Museum of Art, Aug. 15-Sept. 20, 1970, Columbus, Ohio, Columbus Gallery of Fine Arts, Oct. 9-Nov. 1, 1970, Little Rock, Arkansas, Arkansas Art Center, Nov. 21, 1970-Jan. 12, 1971; San Francisco, California, California Palace of the Legion of Honor, *The Armand Hammer Collection*, Feb. 11-Mar. 14, 1971; Oklahoma City, Oklahoma, Oklahoma Art Center, *The Armand Hammer Collection*, June 15-July 11, 1971; San Diego, California, Fine Arts Gallery of San Diego, *The Armand Hammer Collection*, July 23-Sept. 5, 1971

Literature: Sale catalog, *Catalogue des Tableaux, Pastels et Dessins par Edgar Degas*, 2nd sale, Paris: Galerie Georges Petit, 1918, no. 92, p. 51, repr.; Sale catalog, *Catalogue de la Vente F. R.*, Paris: Hôtel Drouot, Mar. 8, 1930, 2nd part, no. 74, p. 20, repr.; P. A. Lemoisne, *Degas et Son Oeuvre*, Paris: 1947, vol. III, p. 636, no. 1100, repr.; Sale catalog, *Impressionist and Modern Paintings*, London: Sotheby & Co., Dec. 10, 1969, no. 20, repr. in color

This picture is similar in size and conception to the Louvre

Dancers in Blue which is, in turn, closely related to the Metropolitan *Dancers in Red and Green*. The Louvre picture and this one seem, in fact, to be coloristic variations on the same theme, the Louvre painting developed in blue-green-purple, this one in red-yellow-orange. The broadly stippled background was explored by Degas in other pictures at this time, both of dancers (Lemoisne 975) and of bathers (Lemoisne 1104). The placement of the figures suggests the same or similar poses seen from different angles of vision, a device increasingly exploited by Degas. Along with his interest in different poses arranged sequentially, the resulting proto-cinematic effect almost certainly reflects his knowledge of early experiments in motion photography. This effect is enhanced by the suggestion of unstable equilibrium resulting from the eccentric arangement of the figures. The entire composition is stabilized by Degas' manipulation of his hues and their values.

28   Gustave Moreau (1826-1898)
King David
Oil on canvas: 90⁹/₁₆" x 54⁵/₁₆" (230.0 x 137.6 cm.)

Collections: Comtesse Roederer, Paris; Hector Brame, Paris; Walter P. Chrysler, Jr., New York

Exhibitions: Paris, *Exposition Universelle Internationale*, 1878, no. 659; Toronto, The Art Gallery of Ontario, *The Sacred and Profane in Symbolist Art*, Nov. 1969, no. 64; New York, Spencer A. Samuels & Co., Ltd., *Symbolists*, Nov. 1970, no. 116; San Francisco, California, California Palace of the Legion of Honor, *The Armand Hammer Collection*, Feb. 11-Mar. 14, 1971; Oklahoma City, Oklahoma, Oklahoma Art Center, *The Armand Hammer Collection*, June 15-July 11, 1971

Literature: Dubosc de Pesquidoux, *L'Art dans les Deux Mondes, L'Art du XIXᵉᵐᵉ Siècle, Peinture et Sculpture*, Paris: E. Plon et Cie., 1881, vol. 1, no. VI, p. 84; Léon Deshairs, *L'Art de Nôtre Temps, Gustave Moreau*, Paris: Librairie Central des Beaux-Arts, no. XXXIII, pp. 79-80, repr. opp.; *Catalogue Officiel de l'Exposition Universelle Internationale*, Paris: Commissariat Général, Imprimerie Nationale, 1878, vol. I (Oeuvres d'Art), no. 659, p. 51; "L'Art Moderne à l'Exposition de 1878," *Gazette des Beaux-Arts*, Paris: A. Quantin, 1879, pp. 31-33; Pierre de Savarus, *Dix Années d'Art (Souvenir des Expositions)*, Paris: 1879, pp. 94-95; Claude Phillips, "Gustave Moreau," *Magazine of Art*, 1885, pp. 228-233, repr.; Paul Leprieur, "Gustave Moreau et Son Oeuvre," *L'Artiste*, Paris: Mar.-June 1889, p. 40; Jean Lorrain, *Sensations et Souvenirs*, Paris: 1895, p. 67; Ary Renan, *Gustave Moreau*, Paris: Imprimerie Georges Petit, 1900, pp. 71, 73, repr. (etching by M. Bracquemond); Henri Frantz, "The New Moreau Gallery," *The Magazine of Art*, London: Cassell & Co., Ltd., 1900, pp. 97-104, repr. p. 98 (engraving by Jonnard reprinted from Claude Phillips, "Gustave Moreau," *The Magazine of

Art*, 1885, pp. 228-233); Gustave Larroumet, Institute de France, Académie des Beaux-Arts, *Notices Historiques sur la Vie et les Oeuvres de M. Gustave Moreau*, Paris: Firmin-Didot et Cie., 1901, p. 36; *Catalogue Sommaire des Peintures, Dessins, Cartons et Aquarelles du Musée Gustave Moreau*, Paris: Imprimerie Réunies, 1902, pp. 9, 22, 33, 49, 50, 55, 113; Louis Dimier, "L'Inspiration de Gustave Moreau," *Minerva*, no. 18, Paris: Nov. 15, 1902, p. 276; Camille Mauclair, "The Gustave Moreau Museum in Paris," *The Art Journal*, London: 1905, p. 255, repr.; Musée Nationale de Gustave Moreau, *Principales Oeuvres de Maître dans les Musées et Collections Particulières* (preface Georges Desvallières), Paris: J. E. Bulloz, 1906, no. 22 in portfolio (heliograph by J. Chauvet); Jean Laran and Léon Deshairs, "Gustave Moreau," *L'Art de Nôtre Temps*, Paris: 1913, pp. 79-80, pl. XXXII; Anonymous, "Gustave Moreau," *Les Peintres Illustres*, no. 55, Paris: Pierre Lafitte, 1914, p. 74; Ragnar van Holten, *L'Art Fantastique de Gustave Moreau*, Paris: Jean-Jacques Pauvert, 1906, pl. 37; Spencer A. Samuels, *Symbolists*, New York: Spencer A. Samuels & Co. Ltd., 1970, no. 116, p. 56, repr.

Originally known simply as *David*, this picture has more recently borne the title *King David Meditating*. In it one sees that juxtaposition of disparate architectural and decorative elements so dear to Moreau. The cross-decorated temple lamp and the evangelist symbols on the capitals may perhaps indicate a Christian, specifically Catholic, interpretation of David as a prototype of Christ. Further, the painting borders on being an allegory of the senses, with the aged psalmist surrounded by flowers, incense, and a burning lamp and clothed in jewels and rich materials. The subtle rhythms of the asymmetrical composition and the softening of the delicate and intricate detail in a poetic atmosphere distinguish Moreau's salon paintings like the *King David* from the empty formalism and banal sentiments of so many of his academic contemporaries. Of this kind of picture, Ary Renan wrote in the *Gazette des Beaux-Arts* in 1899: "His (Moreau's) idea was to equal, without deranging the harmony of line, and by the prestige alone of environing decorations, all the suggestions provoked in literature, music and the theater."

29   Gustave Moreau (1826-1898)
Salome, 1876
Oil on canvas: 56⅝" x 41¹/₁₆" (143.8 x 104.2 cm.)

Collections: Louis Mante, Marseilles (Sale, Paris, Galerie Charpentier, Nov. 28, 1956, no. 10); Robert Lebel, Paris; Julius Weitzner, London, 1958; Huntington Hartford, New York

Exhibitions: Paris, *Salon of 1876*, no. 1506; Paris, *Exposition Universelle Internationale*, 1878, no. 657; Paris, Galerie Georges Petit, *Gustave Moreau Exposition au Profit des Oeuvres du Travail et des Pauvres Honteux*, 1906, no. 76, (lent by Louis Mante) ; Paris, Musée du Louvre, *Gustave Moreau*, June, 1961, no. 22 (lent by Huntington Hartford); New York, Museum of Modern Art, Dec. 4, 1961-Feb. 4, 1962, and Chicago, Art Institute of Chicago, Mar. 2-Apr. 15, 1962, *Odilon Redon—Gustave Moreau—Rudolphe Bresdin*, no. 177 (lent by Huntington Hartford); Oklahoma City, Oklahoma, Oklahoma Art Center, *The Armand Hammer Collection*, June 15-July 11, 1971; San Diego, California, Fine Arts Gallery of San Diego, *The Armand Hammer Collection*, July 23-Sept. 5, 1971

Literature: *Salon de 1876, Palais de Champs Elysées, Explication des Ouvrages*, Paris: Imprimerie Nationale, May 1, 1876, no. 1506, p. 187; P. de Saint Victor, *La Liberté*, May 19, 1876; *Zigzags, Salon de 1876, Gustave Moreau*, June 25, 1876, no. 9, p. 2; Charles Yriarte, "Le Salon de 1876," *Gazette des Beaux-Arts*, Paris: Imprimerie Nationale, 6th ed., vol. 13, pp. 705-708, p. 698, repr. (sketch for *Salome)*; Pierre de Savarus, *Le Salon de 1876, à Vol d'Oiseau*, Paris: Chez Dentu, 1876, pp. 43, 44; George Dufour, "Le Grande Art et le Petit Art du Salon de 1876," *L'Artiste*, Amiens: Typographie Delattre-Lenoel, pp. 24, 25; Victor de Swarte, *Lettres sur le Salon de 1876*, Saint Omer: Imprimerie Fleury-Le Maire, 1876, p. 79; *Catalogue Officiel de l'Exposition Universelle Internationale de 1878 à Paris*, published by the Commissariat General, Paris: Imprimerie Nationale, vol. I, section I (Oeuvres d'Art), no. 657, p. 51; Paul Mantz, "Paris Exposition Universelle, La Peinture Française," *Gazette des Beaux-Arts*, vol. I, Dec. 1, 1878, p. 47; Charles L. Duval, *Les Beaux-Arts à l'Exposition de 1878, Impression et Notes d'Artistes*, Meaux: Librairie Ch. Cochet, 1878, p. 127 (from *Le Publicateur*, Arrondissemont de Meaux); *Exposition Universelle de Paris, 1878, Le Livre d'Or des Exposants*, Section I (Beaux-Arts), Paris: André Sagnier, 1878, p. 10; Hippolyte Gautier and Adrien Desprez, *Les Curiosités de l'Exposition de 1878*, Paris: Librairie Charles Delagrave, 1878, p. 87; *Les Artistes Français à l'Exposition Universelle de 1878*, Paris: Georges Décaux, ed., p. 56; M. E. Bergerat, *Les Chefs-d'oeuvre d'Art à l'Exposition Universelle, 1878*, Paris: Ludovic Baschet, 1878, p. 156, repr. pl. 20 (photogravure Goupil et Cie.); Paul Mantz, "L'Art Moderne à l'Exposition de 1878," *Gazette des Beaux-Arts*, Paris: A. Quantin, 1879, pp. 31, 33; Pierre de Savarus, *Dix Années D'Art (Souvenir des Expositions)*, Paris: 1879, pp. 89-91; Dubosc de Pesquidoux, *L'Art dans les Deux Mondes —Peinture et Sculpture, L'Art au XIXeme Siècle*, Paris: E. Plon et Cie., 1881, vol. I, no. IV, p. 82; J. K. Huysman, *A Rebours*, 1884, pp. 71-76; Paul Leprieur, *L'Artiste*, 1889, Mar.: pp. 175, 177, 180, May: pp. 339, 350, 351, June: pp. 444, 449, 450, 452; Jules-Antoine Castagnary, *Salons*, Paris, 1892, vol. II, pp. 227-228; Gustave Larroumet, *Etudes de Litterature et d'Art*, Paris: 1896, pp. 227-278; Léon Thévenin, *L'Esthetique de Gustave Moreau*, Paris: Vanier, 1897, pp. 9, 12-13; Gleeson White, "The Pictures of Gustave Moreau," *The Pageant*, London: 1897, p. 11; Léonce

Benedite, "Deux Idéalistes, Gustave Moreau et E. Burne-Jones," *La Revue de l'Art Ancien et Moderne*, Apr. 1899, pp. 265-290, p. 273, repr.; Ary Renan, "Gustave Moreau," *Gazette des Beaux-Arts*, Paris: Imprimerie Georges Petit, 1900, pp. 62, 63, repr. (heliogravure by J. Chauvet); Gustave Geffroy, *La Vie Artistique*, 6th series, chap. XVI, Paris: H. Floury, 1900, pp. 143-147; Henri Frantz, "The New Gustave Moreau Gallery," *Magazine of Art*, 1900, pp. 99-104; Gustave Larroumet, Institute de France, Académie des Beaux-Arts, *Notice Historique sur la Vie et les Oeuvres de M. Gustave Moreau*, Paris: Firmin-Didot et Cie., 1901, pp. 21, 22, 29, 30, repr. p. 36; Musée National Gustave Moreau, *Principales Oeuvres de Maître dans les Musées et Collections Particulières* (intro. Georges Devallières), Paris: J. E. Bulloz, 1906, no. 9 (heliogravure by J. Chauvet; Mante Coll.); Gustave Geffroy, *L'Oeuvre d'Art, L'Oeuvre de Gustave Moreau*, Paris: Imprimerie L. Lambert, 1906, pp. 5, 9, 26, 27; Catalog, Galerie Georges Petit, *Exposition Gustave Moreau, Au Profit des Oeuvres de Travail et des Pauvres Honteux* (preface Robert de Montesquiou), Paris: Imprimerie Georges Petit, 1906, no. 76, p. 38 (Mante Coll., Marseilles); Arthur Symons, *Studies in Seven Arts*, London: 1910, pp. 73-77; Léon Deshairs and Jean Laran, *L'Art de Nôtre Temps, Gustave Moreau*, Paris: Librarie Centrale des Beaux-Arts, 1913, pl. XXVIII, pp. 71, 72, repr. opp.; Musée National Gustave Moreau, *L'Oeuvre de Gustave Moreau* (intro. Georges Desvallières), Paris: Bulloz, 1913, no. 9, repr.; Anonymous, *Gustave Moreau (Les Peintres Illustres, no. 55)*, Paris: Pierre Lafitte, 1914, pp. 69-70; *Lettres de Georges Rouault et André Suarès, Gustave Moreau, L'Art et Les Artistes*, no. 66, Apr. 1926, Paris: Armand Dayot, p. 223 repr.; Sale catalog, *Catalogue de la Vente Collection Louis Mante*, Galerie Charpentier, Nov. 28, 1956, Paris: Imprimerie M. Schiffer, no. 10, pl. III; Joris-Karl Huysmans, *Against Nature* (translation of *A Rebours*, 1884, by Robert Baldick), Baltimore: Penguin, 1959, pp. 63-67; Ragnar von Holten, *L'Art Fantastique de Gustave Moreau*, Paris: Jean Jacques Pauvert, 1960, pp. 19, 20, pl. III, p. 27, repr. in color; Musée du Louvre, *Catalogue de l'Exposition Gustave Moreau*, Paris: Editions des Musées Nationaux, June 1961, no. 22, p. 22, pl. II (Huntington Hartford Coll.); Ragnar von Holten, "Le développement du personnage de Salomé à travers les dessins de Gustave Moreau," *L'Oeil*, Aug. 1961, pp. 44-51, 72; John Rewald, Doré Ashton, and Harold Joachim, *Odilon Redon—Gustave Moreau—Rudolphe Bresdin*, the Museum of Modern Art in collaboration with the Art Institute of Chicago, New York: Doubleday & Co., Inc., 1962, no. 177, p. 116; John Simon, "The Torments of Imagination," *Arts*, Feb. 1962, pp. 20-27, repr.; Daniel Grojnowski, "Les Mystères Gustave Moreau," *Revue Générale des Publications Françaises et Etrangères*, Mar. 1963, vol. 19, no. 190, Editions de Minuit, pp. 225-238 (p. 237: sketch); *Catalogue of Paintings from the Huntington Hartford Collection in the Gallery of Modern*

Art, New York: The Foundation for Modern Art, Inc., 1964, no. 14, repr. in color; Ragnar von Holten, *Gustave Moreau, Symbolist*, Stockholm: Natur och Kultur, 1965, pp. 48-65, repr. p. 49; Max Gérard, *Dali*, New York: Harry N. Abrams, 1968, no. 169, detail repr. in color; Sale catalog: *Important Impressionist and Modern Paintings and Drawings*, New York: Parke-Bernet Galleries, Inc., Mar. 10, 1971, no. 29, p. 52, repr. in color

The best-known version of the artist's best-known subject, *Salome* represents the full flower of the tendency toward accumulation in Moreau's art as well as the apotheosis of one of the most notable and hermetic tendencies in late nineteenth-century French art and literature. This tendency, which involved a slightly overripe enumerative presentation in both visual and verbal media, culminated in and was transformed by the work of Marcel Proust. More than one hundred related drawings are known for Moreau's *Salome* and its variant *The Apparition*, of which the finished watercolor, now in the Louvre, was also exhibited in the Salon of 1876. The figure of Salome herself was studied in a wooden lay figure covered with wax and dressed, one of the dozen or so surviving pieces of sculpture by Moreau. Holten believes the subject to have been inspired by Flaubert's *Salammbô*, while Duthuit traces it to Mallarmé's *Herodiade*, but perhaps no specific source is needed for this theme of the *belle dame sans merci* (cf. Mario Praz, *The Romantic Agony*) so common to the fin de siècle. Daffner has pointed out that Moreau's interpretation of the Orpheus myth, the poet's severed head lying on a lyre, is closely related to the Salome theme *(Salome*, Munich, 1912, p. 289). The scene takes place under the surveillance of the Ephesian Artemis in a fantastic architecture of Moorish inspiration. J. K. Huysmans, who placed the painting in the possession of Des Esseintes, hero of *A Rebours*, described Salome as follows: "Her face composed, solemn, almost august, she begins the lascivious dance which must awaken the deadened senses of the aged Herod . . . . Concentrating, her eyes fixed like those of a sleep-walker, she sees neither the trembling Tetrarch nor her mother, the fierce Herodiade, who watches her, nor the hermaphrodite, or eunuch, who stands, sword in hand, at the foot of the throne." Moreau himself described Salome as, "That woman nonchalantly strolling . . . in the gardens recently stained by that horrible murder which terrified the executioner himself." Kaplan has called this picture, which has been known variously as *Salome*, the *Dance of Salome*, and *Salome Dancing Before Herod*, Moreau's "most successful synthesis of precise delineation and free handling of oil pigment."

30 Paul Cézanne (1839-1906)
Boy Resting, ca. 1885
Oil on canvas: 21⁷/₁₆" x 25¹³/₁₆" (54.5 x 65.5 cm.)

Collections: Ambroise Vollard, Paris; Galerie Bernheim-Jeune, Paris; Galerie Thannhauser, Lucerne; Josef Stransky, New York; Estate of Josef Stransky (on loan to the Worcester Art Museum, Worcester, Massachusetts, June 1, 1932-Mar. 9, 1936); Wildenstein & Co., Inc., New York; Arnold Kirkeby, New York (Sale, New York, Parke-Bernet Galleries, Inc., Nov. 19, 1958, no. 16); Mrs. Arnold Kirkeby, Los Angeles

Exhibitions: Paris, Galerie Bernheim-Jeune, *Rétrospective Paul Cézanne*, June 1-30, 1926, no. 5; New York, Museum of Modern Art, *1st Loan Exhibition*, Nov. 1929, no. 13; Chicago, Art Institute of Chicago, *A Century of Progress*, June 1-Nov. 1, 1933, no. 318A; Worcester, Massachusetts, Worcester Art Museum, *The Loan Exhibition of the New Museum Building*, 1933-1934; San Francisco, California Palace of the Legion of Honor, *French Painting from the 15th Century to the Present Day*, June 8-July 8, 1934, no. 65; Kansas City, Missouri, William Rockhill Nelson Gallery of Art, *Nineteenth Century French Painting*, Mar. 15-Apr. 12, 1936; London, Wildenstein & Co., Ltd., *Collection of a Collector, Modern Painting from Ingres to Matisse, The Private Collection of the Late Josef Stransky*, July 1936, no. 18; Toledo, Ohio, Toledo Museum of Art, *Cézanne, Gauguin*, Nov. 1-Dec. 13, 1936, no. 29; San Francisco, San Francisco Museum of Art, *Paul Cézanne*, Sept. 1-Oct. 4, 1937, no. 16 (repr.); London, Wildenstein & Co., Ltd., *Homage to Paul Cézanne*, July 1939, no. 30; New Haven, Connecticut, Yale University Art Gallery, *Cézanne and the French Tradition*, Jan. 29-Feb. 18, 1945; Cincinnati, Cincinnati Art Museum, *Paintings by Paul Cézanne*, Feb. 5-Mar. 9, 1947, no. 4 (repr. pl. 4), (lent by Wildenstein & Co. Ltd.); New York, Wildenstein & Co., Inc., *A Loan Exhibition of Paul Cézanne for the Benefit of the New York Infirmary* (lent by Estate of Josef Stransky), Mar. 27-Apr. 26, 1947, no. 19; Los Angeles, Art Galleries, University of California, *California Collects: North and South*, Jan. 20-Feb. 23, 1958, no. 29 (repr.); Oklahoma City, Oklahoma, Oklahoma Art Center, *The Armand Hammer Collection*, June 15-July 11, 1971; San Diego, California, Fine Arts Gallery of San Diego, *The Armand Hammer Collection*, July 23-Sept. 5, 1971

Literature: *Kunst und Künstler*, 1926, XXIV, pp. 448-449; Eugenio d'Ors, *Paul Cézanne*, Paris: Editions des Chroniques du Jour, 1930, p. 25, repr., table: no. VI; *International Studio*, Nov. 1929, p. 66, repr.; Ralph Flint, "The Private Collection of Josef Stransky," *Art News*, May 16, 1931, p. 8, repr.; Perry B. Cott, "The Stransky Collection of Modern Art," *Bulletin of the Worcester Art Museum*, winter 1933, p. 157; Nina Iavorskaïa, *Paul Cézanne*, Milan, 1935, pl. VI; *Parnassus*, Dec. 1936, p. 26, repr.; *Art Digest*, Apr. 1, 1936, p. 5, repr.; Maurice Raynal, *Cézanne*, New York, 1936, pl. 51; Lionello Venturi, *Cézanne, Son Art—Son Oeuvre*, Paris: Paul Rosenberg, 1936, vol. I, p. 150, no. 391, vol. II, pl. 107, no. 391, repr.; Ambroise Vollard, *Paul Cézanne, His Life and Art* (trans. Harold L. Van Doren), New York, 1937, pl. 9; *Art News*, Oct. 1958, p. 41, repr.; "Kirkeby Collection at Auction," *Arts*, Nov. 1958, p. 27, repr.; *Connoisseur*, Nov. 1958, p. 124, repr.; Robert Melville, "Exhibitions," *Architectural Review*, Aug. 1959, pp. 131-133, repr.; *Connoisseur*, Jan. 1959, p. 254, repr.; *Apollo*, June 1959, p. 215, repr.; Mark Roskill, *Van Gogh, Gauguin, and the Impressionist Circle*, Greenwich, 1970, p. 231, repr., pl. 179; Elie Faure, *Cézanne*, Paris: Braun & Cie (Collections des Maîtres), n.d., pl. 7; *French Masters of the XIX and XX Century; The Private Collection of J. Stransky, N. Y., including recent accessions up to May 1935* (reprint), New York, n.d., repr.

This picture of a reclining clothed figure, unique in Cézanne's oeuvre, has been known variously as *The Siesta, Boy by the Brook, Reclining Boy,* and *Boy Resting.* Venturi refers to its subject as a peasant, but Vollard is said to have considered it a portrait of the artist's son Paul. The latter seems not unlikely. It exemplifies as well as any of his paintings the artist's struggle to reconcile pictorial and naturalistic scale and effect. The broad rectilinear paint areas at the top of the canvas were clearly conceived by Cézanne as flat elements directly related to the size and shape of that canvas. Their two-dimensional strength creates a pictorial pressure which jeopardizes the human identity of the figure, makes its location in depth ambiguous, and mitigates its three-dimensionality. That Cézanne could explore such complex problems without sacrificing the quality of his art is an index of his genius.

31 Henri de Toulouse-Lautrec (1864-1901)
In the Salon, 1894
Oil on cardboard, 15¾" x 23⅞" (40.0 x 60.6 cm.)
Signed lower left: H.-T. Lautrec

Collections: Octave Maus, Brussels (acquired from the artist about 1896); Tetze-Lund, Copenhagen; J. K. Thannhauser, New York; Paul Rosenberg, New York; Sale, London, Sotheby & Co., Nov. 7, 1962, no. 85 repr. in color; Galerie Beyeler, Basel; Hammer Galleries, New York

Exhibitions: Paris, Galerie Manzi et Joyant, *Toulouse-Lautrec,* 1896; Brussels, *Exposition Toulouse-Lautrec,* organized by La Libre Esthétique, Mar. 1902; Paris, Gallerie Manzi et Joyant, *Exposition Retrospective de L'Oeuvre de H. Toulouse-Lautrec,* June 15-July 11, 1914, no. 39; New York, Hammer Galleries, *40th Anniversary Loan Exhibition, 1928-1968,* Nov. 7-Dec. 7, 1968 (repr. in color in cat. p. 54); Memphis, Tennessee, Brooks Memorial Art Gallery, *The Armand Hammer Collection,* Oct. 2-Dec. 30, 1969, no. 58 (repr. in cat.); Washington, D. C., Smithsonian Institution, *The Armand Hammer Collection,* Mar. 20-May 17, 1970, no. 64 (repr. in cat. in color); Smithsonian Institution Traveling Exhibition Service, *The Armand Hammer Collection,* Kansas City,

Missouri, William Rockhill Nelson Gallery of Art, June 30-Aug. 2, 1970, New Orleans, Louisiana, Isaac Delgado Museum of Art, Aug. 15-Sept. 20, 1970, Columbus, Ohio, Columbus Gallery of Fine Arts, Oct. 9-Nov. 1, 1970, Little Rock, Arkansas, Arkansas Art Center, Nov. 21, 1970-Jan. 12, 1971; San Francisco, California, California Palace of the Legion of Honor, *The Armand Hammer Collection,* Feb. 11-Mar. 14, 1971; Oklahoma City, Oklahoma, Oklahoma Art Center, *The Armand Hammer Collection,* June 15-July 11, 1971; San Diego, California, Fine Arts Gallery of San Diego, *The Armand Hammer Collection,* July 23-Sept. 5, 1971

Literature: Maurice Joyant, *Henri de Toulouse-Lautrec,* Paris: H. Floury, 1926, p. 286; Gotthard Jedlicka, *Henri de Toulouse-Lautrec,* Erienbach-Zurich: E. Rentsch, 1943, p. 321, repr. opp. p. 218; Francis Jourdin and Jean Adhémar, *Toulouse-Lautrec,* Paris: P. Tisné, 1952, repr. pl. 84; Sale catalog, *Impressionist and Modern Paintings, Drawings, and Sculpture,* London, Sotheby & Co., Nov. 7, 1962, no. 85, repr. in color; P. Huisman and M. G. Dortu, *Lautrec by Lautrec,* New York: Viking Press, 1964, pp. 130-131, repr. in color; *Apollo,* Sept. 1966, p. LXXV, repr.; "On the Market," *Apollo,* Nov. 1968, p. 395, repr.; François Daulte, "Hammer en dix chefs-d'oeuvre," *Connaissance des Arts,* Sept. 1970, p. 79, repr.; *Connoisseur,* Nov. 1970, p. 210, repr.

From 1892 until 1895 Tolouse-Lautrec produced a series of pictures of prostitutes and bordello scenes. The summation of this work was the large canvas *Au salon de la rue des Moulins* painted in 1894 and now in the museum at Albi. There is a pastel version of the complete composition in the same museum and a large group of related studies of which this picture is one. Presumably also executed in 1894, it represents the same two women who are seated at the left rear center of the Albi painting. According to Joyant, the woman seen in profile is the Rolande of several of the other studies. In transferring the figures to the larger work Lautrec has altered only the positions of the arms. The technique of this study is much broader than that of the finished picture, and its color is worked out in terms of close-valued, close-hued, and astringent contrasts in Lautrec's most expressive manner. Octave Maus is said to have acquired this picture in 1896, perhaps directly from the Manzi-Joyant exhibition at which the bordello scenes were shown by Lautrec in two small locked rooms.

32 Emile Bernard (1868-1941)
Wheat Harvest
Oil on canvas: 28½" x 35⅞" (72.4 x 91.1 cm.)
Signed and dated lower left: Bernard 1889

Collections: Clement Altarriba (son-in-law of the artist), Paris; Wildenstein & Co., Inc., New York; Mr. and Mrs. Richard Sussman, New York; Findlay Galleries, Inc., Chicago

Exhibitions: Memphis, Tennessee, Brooks Memorial Art Gallery, *The Armand Hammer Collection*, Oct. 2-Dec. 30, 1969, no. 62 (repr. in cat.); Washington, D. C., Smithsonian Institution, *The Armand Hammer Collection*, Mar. 20-May 17, 1970, no. 69 (repr. in cat. in color); Smithsonian Institution Traveling Exhibition Service, *The Armand Hammer Collection*, Kansas City, Missouri, William Rockhill Nelson Gallery of Art, June 30-Aug. 2, 1970, New Orleans, Louisiana, Isaac Delgado Museum of Art, Aug. 15-Sept. 20, 1970, Columbus, Ohio, Columbus Gallery of Fine Arts, Oct. 9-Nov. 1, 1970, Little Rock, Arkansas, Arkansas Art Center, Nov. 21, 1970-Jan. 12, 1971; San Francisco, California, California Palace of the Legion of Honor, *The Armand Hammer Collection*, Feb. 11-Mar. 14, 1971; Oklahoma City, Oklahoma, Oklahoma Art Center, *The Armand Hammer Collection*, June 15-July 11, 1971; San Diego, California, Fine Arts Gallery of San Diego, *The Armand Hammer Collection*, July 23-Sept. 5, 1971

Literature: John Rewald, *Post Impressionism*, New York: Museum of Modern Art, 1956, repr. p. 285; *Connoisseur*, Nov. 1966, repr. p. XCIII; *Art Journal*, Winter 1966-1967, repr. p. 195

The harvesting of wheat was among the favorite themes of the group gathered around Gauguin in Brittany during the years 1888-1890. Bernard had treated the subject in painting in 1888 and in a print in 1889, the year of this picture, and Gauguin had also painted Breton haymakers in 1889 (cf. his *Breton Landscape* in the de Sylva Collection of the Los Angeles County Museum of Art). Bernard, forbidden by his father to join Gauguin at Pont Aven, passed the summer of 1889 at Saint-Briac where this picture was probably painted. One sees in the flat color areas reminiscences of the Japanese prints so popular with the Pont-Aven group, and in the outlining of the shapes the "cloisonnism" identified in their work by Edouard Dujardin. At this particular moment Bernard had carried flatness and clear separation of colors considerably further than Gauguin, although his facture (and Gauguin's of the period) recalls Cézanne's version of the Impressionist comma-like brushwork with its groups of parallel strokes. In the cross on the distant hill one can perhaps see a forecast of the mystical Catholicism that was increasingly to occupy Bernard.

33   Paul Gauguin (1848-1903)
Bonjour M. Gauguin
Oil on canvas, mounted on panel
29½" x 21½" (74.9 x 54.6 cm.)
Inscribed lower left: Bonjour M. Gauguin

Collections: Mme. Marie Henry, Le Pouldu; Galerie Barbazanges, Paris; Meyer Goodfriend, New York (Sale, New York, American Art Galleries, Jan. 4-5, 1923, no. 107); B. M. Alexander, New York; Howard Young Galleries, New York; Carlton Mitchell, Annapolis; Count Ivan Podgoursky, San Antonio; Mrs. Mary Ermolaev, Princeton (Sale, Geneva, Christie, Manson & Woods, Nov. 6, 1969, no. 169, repr.)

Exhibitions: Paris, Galerie Barbazanges, *Exposition d'Oeuvres Inconnues*, Oct. 10-30, 1919, no. 2; New York, Wildenstein & Co., Inc., *A Retrospective Loan Exhibition for the Benefit of Les Amies de Paul Gauguin and the Penn Normal Industrial and Agricultural School*, Mar. 2-Apr. 18, 1936, no. 14; Montreal, Museum of Fine Arts, *Manet to Matisse*, May-June, 1949, no. 14; Paris, Galerie Loize, *Les Amitiés de Monfried et ses reliques de Gauguin*, May 11, 1951, no. 108 (inaugurated by Georges Salles, Director of the Museums of France); Houston, Museum of Fine Arts, *Paul Gauguin, His Place in the Meeting of East and West*, Mar. 27-Apr. 25, 1954, no. 15; Wichita Falls, The Museum Association of Midwestern Universities, Sept.-Oct. 1955, no. 16; Tulsa, Philbrook Art Center, *Four Centuries of European Art*, Oct. 1956, no. 34; Oklahoma City, Oklahoma Art Center, *Four Centuries of European Art*, Nov. 1957, no. 23; Little Rock, Arkansas, Museum of Fine Arts, Dec. 1958, no. 30; Phoenix Art Museum, *One Hundred Years of French Painting, 1860-1960*, Feb. 1-26, 1961, no. 42 (lent by Count Ivan Podgoursky, San Antonio, Texas); Oakland, California, Art Museum, *One Hundred Years of French Painting, 1860-1960*, Mar. 5-31, 1961, no. 42; New York, Christie, Manson & Woods (U.S.A.) Ltd., *Van Gogh, Gauguin and Their Circle*, Nov. 1968, no. 9; Memphis, Tennessee, Brooks Memorial Art Gallery, *The Armand Hammer Collection*, Dec. 19, 1969-Jan. 18, 1970; Washington, D.C., Smithsonian Institution, *The Armand Hammer Collection*, Mar. 20, May 17, 1970, no. 57 (repr. in cat. in color); Smithsonian Institution Traveling Exhibition Service, *The Armand Hammer Collection*, Kansas City, Missouri, William Rockhill Nelson Gallery of Art, June 30-Aug. 2, 1970, New Orleans, Louisiana, Isaac Delgado Museum of Art, Aug. 15-Sept. 20, 1970, Columbus, Ohio, Columbus Gallery of Fine Arts, Oct. 9-Nov. 1, 1970, Little Rock, Arkansas, Arkansas Art Center, Nov. 21, 1970-Jan. 12, 1971; San Francisco, California Palace of the Legion of Honor, *The Armand Hammer Collection*, Feb. 11-Mar. 14, 1971; Oklahoma City, Oklahoma, Oklahoma Art Center, *The Armand Hammer Collection*, June 15-July 11, 1971; San Diego, California, Fine Arts Gallery of San Diego, *The Armand Hammer Collection*, July 23-Sept 5, 1971

Literature: Charles Chassé, *Gauguin et le Groupe de Pont-Aven*, Paris: H. Floury, 1921, pp. 48-50; *American Art Journal*, 1923-24, vol. 20, p. 275; Jean de Rotonchamp, *Gauguin*, Paris: Les Editions G. Crès et Cie, 1925, p. 70; *Canadian Art*, Summer 1949, vol. VI, no. 4, p. 176, repr.; J. Loize, *Les Amitiés du peintre Georges-Daniel de Monfried et ses réliques de Gauguin*, 1951, no. 108, pp. 86-87; Charles Chassé, *Gauguin et son Temps*, 1955, pp. 70, 79; M. Malingue, "Du Nouveau sur Gauguin," *L'Oeil*, July-Aug. 1959, p. 38; John Rewald, *Le Post-Impressionisme*, Paris:

Albin Michel, 1961, p. 176; George Baudaille, *Gauguin*, London: 1964, pp. 89, 130, repr. in color; Georges Wildenstein, *Gauguin Oeuvre Catalogue*, Paris: 1964, no. 321, pp 121-122; *Art in America*, Sept. 1969, p. 15, repr.; *Art News*, Sept. 1969, p. 26, repr.; *Apollo*, Oct. 1969, p. IX, repr.; *Connaissance des Arts*, Oct. 1969, p. 67, repr.; *Apollo*, Feb. 1970, p. 170, repr.; *Connoisseur*, Feb. 1970, p. 116, repr.; Frank Davis, "A Royal Record of Portraiture," *Country Life*, Feb. 5, 1970, pp. 302-303, repr.

In 1889 Gauguin and the painters working with him transferred their Breton activities from Pont Aven to Le Pouldu, which they found more primitive. In October of that year they moved to an inn kept by Marie Henry and soon thereafter began decorating its walls with paintings and sculpture. Gauguin's *Bonjour Monsieur Gauguin* occupied the upper panel of a door in the inn. There are two existing versions of the composition, and both Wildenstein and Sutton are agreed that the Hammer picture is the one originally fastened to the door at Le Pouldu while the Prague version precedes it or is a later replica. In any case, the two pictures cannot have been created more than a few weeks apart. This picture is distinguished from the Prague version by a somewhat more unified composition and more consistent brushwork. The subject was almost certainly inspired by Courbet's *Bonjour Monsieur Courbet* which Gauguin and van Gogh had seen on a visit to Montpellier in December 1888. A related watercolor on silk (Rewald, *Gauguin Drawings*, no. 18) is apparently a study for the righthand figure in the Prague version.

34 Vincent van Gogh (1853-1890)
Garden of the Rectory at Nuenen, 1885
Oil on canvas, mounted on panel
20⅞" x 30¾" (53.0 x 78.2 cm.)

Collections: Oldenzeel Gallery, Rotterdam, 1903; Jan Smit, Alblasserdam (Sale, Amsterdam, Mak van Waaij, Feb. 10, 1919, no. 30, repr.); L. J. Smit, Kinderdijk; Leo C. Smit, Kinderdijk, 1952; (Sale, New York, Parke-Bernet Galleries, Inc., Nov. 20, 1968, no. 37); Spencer Samuel & Co., Ltd., New York; Fletcher Jones, Los Angeles

Exhibitions: Rotterdam, Oldenzeel Gallery, *Van Gogh*, 1904, no. 31; The Hague, Gemeentemuseum, *Vincent van Gogh*, Mar. 30-May 17, 1953, no. 31; Otterloo, Rijksmuseum Kröller-Müller, *Vincent van Gogh*, May 24-July 19, 1953, no. 18; Amsterdam, Stedelijk Museum, *Vincent van Gogh*, July 23-Sept. 20, 1953, no. 18; Dordrecht, Dordrecht Museum, *Boem, Bloem en Plant*, July 16-Aug. 31, 1955, no. 52; Paris, Musée Jacquemart-André, *Vincent van Gogh*, Feb.-Mar. 1960, no. 11, p. 30; Washington, D. C., Smithsonian Institution, *The Armand Hammer Collection*, Mar. 20-May 17, 1970; Smithsonian Institution Traveling Exhibition Service, *The Armand Hammer Collection*,

Kansas City, Missouri, William Rockhill Nelson Gallery of Art, June 30-Aug. 2, 1970, New Orleans, Louisiana, Isaac Delgado Museum of Art, Aug. 15-Sept. 20, 1970, Columbus, Ohio, Columbus Gallery of Fine Arts, Oct. 9-Nov. 1, 1970, Little Rock, Arkansas, Arkansas Art Center, Nov. 21, 1970-Jan. 12, 1971, no. 106 (repr. in cat. supplement); San Francisco, California, California Palace of the Legion of Honor, *The Armand Hammer Collection*, Feb. 11-Mar. 14, 1971; Oklahoma City, Oklahoma, Oklahoma Art Center, *The Armand Hammer Collection*, June 15-July 11, 1971; San Diego, California, Fine Arts Gallery of San Diego, *The Armand Hammer Collection*, July 23-Sept. 5, 1971

Literature: *Vincent van Gogh, Brieven aan Zijn Broeder* (ed. J. van Gogh-Bonger), Amsterdam: 1914, Letter 394, vol. II, p. 463; *The Letters of Vincent van Gogh to His Brother*, London: Constable & Co., Ltd., New York: Houghton Mifflin, 1927, Letter 394, pp. 456-458; J. B. de la Faille, *L'Oeuvre de Vincent van Gogh, Catalogue Raisonné*, Paris and Brussels: Editions G. van Oest, 1928, vol. I, no. 67, vol. II, pl. XX (measurements incorrect); Dr. Walter Vanbeselaere, *De Hollandsche Periode (1880-1885) in Het Werk van Vincent van Gogh*, Antwerp: De Sikkel, 1937, pp. 294, 352, 414; J. B. de la Faille, *Vincent van Gogh*, Paris: Hyperion Press, 1938, no. 73, p. 79 (measurements incorrect); J. B. de la Faille, *The Works of Vincent van Gogh, His Paintings and Drawings*, Amsterdam: Meulenhoff International, New York: Reynal & Co. with William Morris & Co. Inc., 1970, no. F67, pp. 66, 614, repr. p. 67; Sale catalog, *Impressionist and Modern Paintings and Sculptures*, London: Sotheby & Co., Apr. 15, 1970, no. 26, p. 55, repr. opp. in color

In the late winter of 1885-86 van Gogh wrote to his brother that, "When there was snow, I . . . painted a few studies of our garden," and de la Faille dates this picture to January 1885. The scene is taken from the presbytery at Nuenen, the small town in which van Gogh's father was vicar and where Vincent lived with his family for two years before going to France. The distant tower occurs in several pictures of the time, and there exist another painting and two drawings directly related to this scene (de la Faille 185, 1133, 1234). The picture projects the bleakness Vincent felt around him in the winter of 1885, a bleakness which permeates both his landscapes and his figure studies. It is among the last of his "Dutch" pictures, worked out in the dark tonalities of the Hague school, its drawing perhaps indebted to the English illustration he knew so well. The extreme lightness of the sky forecasts the future lightening of van Gogh's palette and suggests that interest in color to which he referred constantly in his letters of the period.

35 Vincent van Gogh (1853-1890)
Lilacs, 1887
Oil on canvas: 10¾" x 13¹⁵/₁₆" (27.3 x 35.3 cm.)

Collection: Drs. Fritz and Peter Nathan, Zurich

Exhibitions: Oklahoma City, Oklahoma, Oklahoma Art Center, *The Armand Hammer Collection*, June 15-July 11, 1971; San Diego, California, Fine Arts Gallery of San Diego, *The Armand Hammer Collection*, July 23-Sept. 5, 1971

Literature: J. B. de la Faille, *The Works of Vincent van Gogh, His Paintings and Drawings*, Amsterdam: Meulenhoff International, New York: Reynal & Co. with William Morrow & Co., Inc. 1970, p. 142, no. 286b

Van Gogh had been preoccupied with bringing more intense color into his pictures since well before his move to Paris in 1886. It was only under the direct impact of the paintings he saw in the French capital, however, that he began to use color freely, applying it with an increasingly divisionist brushstroke. Toward the fall of 1887 Vincent wrote to the English painter Levens, "I have lacked money for paying models else I had entirely given myself to figure painting. But I have made a series of color studies in painting, simply flowers, red poppies, blue corn flowers and myosotys, white and rose roses, yellow chrysanthemums—seeking oppositions of blue with orange, red and green, yellow and violet seeking *les tons rompus et neutres* to harmonize brutal extremes. Trying to render intense colour and not a grey harmony." The present picture is no doubt one of these studies.

36 Vincent van Gogh (1853-1890)
The Sower, 1888
Oil on canvas: 13¼" x 15^{15}/$_{16}$" (33.6 x 40.4 cm.)

Collections: Mme. J. van Gogh-Bonger, Amsterdam; Montross Gallery, New York, 1921; Reverend Theodore Pitcairn, Bryn Athyn, Pennsylvania

Exhibitions: New York, Montross Gallery, Oct. 1920; Philadelphia Museum of Art, Summer Loan, 1960 (lent by Rev. Theodore Pitcairn); Memphis, Tennessee, Brooks Memorial Art Gallery, *The Armand Hammer Collection*, Oct. 2-Dec. 30, 1969, no. 54 (repr. in cat.); Washington, D.C., Smithsonian Institution, *The Armand Hammer Collection*, Mar. 20-May 17, 1970, no. 60 (repr. in cat. in color); Smithsonian Institution Traveling Exhibition Service, *The Armand Hammer Collection*, Kansas City, Missouri, William Rockhill Nelson Gallery of Art, June 30-Aug. 2, 1970, New Orleans, Louisiana, Isaac Delgado Museum of Art, Aug. 15-Sept. 20, 1970, Columbus, Ohio, Columbus Gallery of Fine Arts, Oct. 9-Nov. 1, 1970, Little Rock, Arkansas, Arkansas Art Center, Nov. 21-Dec. 12, 1971, San Francisco, California Palace of The Legion of Honor, *The Armand Hammer Collection*, Feb. 11-Mar. 14, 1971; Oklahoma City, Oklahoma, Oklahoma Art Center, *The Armand Hammer Collection*, June 15-July 11, 1971

Literature: J. B. de la Faille, *The Works of Vincent van Gogh, His Paintings and Drawings*, Amsterdam: Meulenhoff International, New York: Reynal & Co. with William Morrow & Co., Inc. 1970, pp. 240, 634, no. 575a, repr. p. 240; Sale catalog, *Important Impressionist and Modern Drawings, Paintings and Sculpture*, London: Christie, Manson & Woods, May 2, 1969, p. 46, no. 58, repr. opp. p. 46

The Sower was a theme which fascinated van Gogh throughout his career, partly because of his Millet-inspired identification with the peasant subject and partly for psychologically more deep-seated associations with fertility and generation. This version of the subject is unique in placing the sower's figure against a silhouette of Arles, something van Gogh otherwise reserved for pictures of reapers or plowed fields (de la Faille 465, 545). The character of the brushwork and the nature and intensity of the color suggest a date in late 1888 or early 1889, conceivably even one as late in 1889 as van Gogh's stay at the hospital of St. Rémy. The size and intensity of the blue-purple field, "compulsive in its excess" (Meyer Schapiro), swallows the figure, adding to the picture's disharmonious scale relationships. These do not, however, detract from the power of this small canvas.

37 Vincent van Gogh (1853-1890)
Hospital at Saint-Rémy, 1889
Oil on canvas: 35½" x 28" (90.2 x 71.1 cm.)

Collections: A. Schuffenecker, Paris; Galerie E. Druet, Paris, 1907; Dr. J. Keller, Paris 1908-10; Galerie E. Druet, Paris, 1910; Paul von Mendelssohn-Bartholdy, Berlin, 1911; Paul Rosenberg & Co., New York; Norton Simon, Los Angeles, 1964 (Sale, New York, Parke-Bernet Galleries, Inc. May 5, 1971, no. 48)

Exhibitions: Paris, Galerie Druet, *Vincent van Gogh*, Jan. 6-18, 1908, no. 16; Berlin, Galerie Paul Cassirer, *Vincent van Gogh*, May-June, 1914, no. 65; Amsterdam, Stedelijk Museum, *Vincent van Gogh en Zijn Tijdgenooten*, Sept. 6-Nov. 2, 1930, no. 92; Frankfurt, Städelsches Kunstinstitut, *Vom Abbild zum Sinnbild*, June 3-July 3, 1931, no. 69; Oklahoma City, Oklahoma, Oklahoma Art Center, *The Armand Hammer Collection*, June 15-July 11, 1971; San Diego, California, Fine Arts Gallery of San Diego, *The Armand Hammer Collection*, July 23-Sept. 5, 1971

Literature: Louis Piérard, *La Vie Tragique de Vincent van Gogh*, Paris: Les Editions G. Crès et Cie., 1924, p. 184, repr.; *Aesculape*, XIIIth Year, II, Nov., 1923, p. 250; Roch Grey, *Vincent van Gogh*, Rome: Editions de Valori Plastici, Imprimerie R. Garroni, repr.; *Aesculape*, XVIth Year, VI, June, 1926, p. 158; Florent Fels, *Vincent van Gogh*, Paris: H. Floury, 1928, p. 171, repr.; J. B. de la Faille, *L'Oeuvre de Vincent van Gogh, Catalogue Raisonné*, Paris and Brussels: Editions G. van Oest, 1928, no. 643, vol. II, pl. CLXXIX; Victor Doiteau and Edgar Leroy, *La Folie de van Gogh* (preface Paul Gachet), Paris: Editions Aesculape, 1928, p. 64, repr. opp.; *The Letters of Vincent van Gogh to His Brother*, Memoir by J. van Gogh-Bonger, London: Constable & Co., Lt., Boston and New York: Houghton Mifflin Co., 1929, vol. III, Letter 610, p. 400; Stedelijk Museum catalog: *Vincent van Gogh en Zijn Trijdgenooten*, Amsterdam: H. G. van Dorssen, 1930, no. 92, p. 18; Städelsches Kunstinstitut catalog: *Austellung von Meisterwerken, Moderner Malerie, Vom Abbild zum Sinnbild*, Frankfurt: August Osterrieth, 1931, no. 69, p. 26; John Rewald, "Van Gogh en Provence," *l'Amour de l'Art*, VIII, Oct., 1936, Paris: Editions A. Sedroswki, p. 297, repr.; W. Scherjon and W. Jos. de Gruyter, *Vincent van Gogh's Great Period*, Amsterdam: "De Spieghel," Ltd., 1937, p. 205, repr.; J. B. de la Faille, *Vincent van Gogh* (preface Charles Terrasse), Paris, London, and New York: Editions Hyperion, 1939, no. 648, p. 446, repr.; Dr. François-Joachim Beer, *Du Demon de van Gogh*, (after *Van Gogh à l'Asile*, by Dr. Edgar Leroy) Nice: Imprimerie Nouvelles Réunis, 1945, p. 75; J. B. de la Faille, *The Works of Vincent van Gogh, His Paintings and Drawings*, Amsterdam: Meulenhoff International, New York: Reynal & Co. with William Morrow & Co., Inc., 1970, no. F643, pp. 256, 636, repr. p. 257; Sale catalog, *Highly Important 19th and 20th Century Paintings, Drawings, and Sculpture, from the Private Collection of Norton Simon*, New York: Parke-Bernet Galleries, Inc., May 5, 1971, no. 48, p. 92, repr. in color

Van Gogh stayed at the hospital at St. Rémy for almost exactly one year, from May 1889 until May 1890, and took its gardens and surroundings as the subject for many of his pictures. In the fall of 1889 he wrote to his brother Theo that he had "two views of the park and the asylum," one of which was undoubtedly this work. Only one other painting (de la Faille 653) shows a substantial portion of the façade of the hospital. One sees in this picture the remnants of an older style in the squared rendering of the building, while the flame-like brushwork of the trees, which Vincent saw as "warped as in old wood," announces the style for which he has become best known. Few of van Gogh's pictures show as well as this the tendency of his brushstrokes to cling to the surface of the canvas or the increasing density and intensity of his paint application during the last three years of his life.

38 Pierre Bonnard (1867-1947)
Street Scene, ca. 1902
Oil on canvas: 21" x 27½" (53.3 x 69.8 cm.)
Signed lower right: Bonnard

Collections: Viscount Jowitt, London; Noel Coward, London; Sale, London, Sotheby & Co., Apr. 18, 1956, no. 14, repr.; Schoneman Galleries, New York; Sale, London, Christie, Manson & Woods, Dec. 1, 1967, p. 34, no. 37, repr.

Exhibitions: Edinburgh Festival, *Bonnard and Vuillard*, Aug. 1948, no. 55 (repr. p. 7); London, Roland, Browse and

Delbanco, *Bonnard*, 1950, no. 16 (repr.); London, Redfern Gallery, *French Paintings*, Oct. 30-Nov. 22, 1952, no. 53; New York, Hammer Galleries, *40th Anniversary Loan Exhibition, 1928-1968*, Nov. 7-Dec. 7, 1968 (repr. in cat. in color p. 10); Memphis, Tennessee, Brooks Memorial Art Gallery, *The Armand Hammer Collection*, Oct. 2-Dec. 30, 1969, no. 59 (repr. in cat.); Washington, D. C., Smithsonian Institution, *The Armand Hammer Collection*, Mar. 20-May 17, 1970, no. 66 (repr. in cat. in color); Smithsonian Institution Traveling Exhibition Service, *The Armand Hammer Collection*, Kansas City, Missouri, William Rockhill Nelson Gallery of Art, June 30-Aug. 2, 1970, New Orleans, Louisiana, Isaac Delgado Museum of Art, Aug. 15-Sept. 20, 1970, Columbus, Ohio, Columbus Gallery of Fine Arts, Oct. 9-Nov. 1, 1970, Little Rock, Arkansas, Arkansas Art Center, Nov. 21, 1970-Jan. 12, 1971; San Francisco, California, California Palace of the Legion of Honor, *The Armand Hammer Collection*, Feb. 11-Mar. 14, 1971; Oklahoma City, Oklahoma, Oklahoma Art Center, *The Armand Hammer Collection*, June 15- July 11, 1971; San Diego, California, Fine Arts Gallery of San Diego, *The Armand Hammer Collection*, July 23-Sept. 5, 1971

Literature: Sale catalog, London: Sotheby & Co., Apr. 18, 1956, no. 144, repr.; *L'Oeil*, no. 21, Sept. 1956, p. 44; Denys Sutton, intro., *Bonnard*, London: Farber Gallery, 1957, p. 12, repr. in color pl. 5; Jean and Henry Dauberville, *Bonnard, Catalogue Raisonné de l'Oeuvre Peint, 1888-1905*, Paris: Bernheim-Jeune, 1965, vol. I, p. 26, no. 269, repr.; Sale catalog, *Important Impressionist and Modern Drawings, Paintings and Sculpture*, London: Christie, Manson & Woods, Dec. 1, 1967, p. 34, no. 37, repr. in color

Although the relatively muted tones, small-scale paint application, and areas of bare canvas in this picture recall the early style Bonnard shared with Vuillard, one already senses the richness of his later color in the red-blue contrasts. The tree trunks hold the composition firmly in place, making it almost a triptych, a favorite Nabi format.

39 Pierre Bonnard (1867-1947)
Nude against the Light, 1909
Oil on canvas: 48¾" x 21½" (123.8 x 54.6 cm.)
Signed lower left: Bonnard

Collections: Galerie Bernheim-Jeune (acquired from the artist Jan. 8, 1909); Henri Bernstein, Paris, Jan. 8, 1910 (Sale, Paris, June 9, 1911); Repurchased by Bernheim-Jeune; Emile Maysisch, Paris; Marianne Feilchenfeldt, Zurich; Ragnar Moltzau, Oslo; Michel P. Couturier, Neuilly-sur-Seine; Adler Collection, London (Sale, New York, Parke-Bernet Galleries, Inc., Mar. 21, 1962, no. 80, repr.); Galerie der Spiegel, Cologne; Alex Léfèvre Gallery, London; Norton Simon (Sale, New York, Parke-Bernet Galleries, Inc., May 5, 1971, no. 59, repr.)

Exhibitions: Zurich, Kunsthaus, *Bonnard*, 1949;
Copenhagen, Ny Carlsberg Glyptotek, *Fra Renoir til Villon,
Franske Malerier eg. Udlaant fra Ragnar Moltzau Samling*,
June 21-Aug. 1, 1956 (hors cat.), and The Hague, Gemeente
Museum, Collection Moltzau, Apr.-June 1957, no. 15;
Edinburgh Festival, and London, Tate Gallery, *Bonnard*,
1958, no. 13; Exposition organized by the Arts Council of
Edinburgh and London, *Documenta III*, 1958, no. 13;
Copenhagen, Ny Carlsberg Glyptotek, 1959; Paris, Galerie
Europe, *Itinéraire sur Trois Générations*, June-July 1960,
no. 4; London, Léfèvre Gallery, *XIXth and XXth Century
French Paintings*, Oct. 14-Nov. 13, 1965, no. 1; Oklahoma
City, Oklahoma, Oklahoma Art Center, *The Armand
Hammer Collection*, June 15-July 11, 1971; San Diego,
California, Fine Arts Gallery of San Diego, *The Armand
Hammer Collection*, July 23-Sept. 5, 1971

Literature: Gustave Coquiot, *Bonnard*, Paris: Editions
Bernheim-Jeune, 1922, pl. 5, repr.; *Art and Auctions*, vol. 6,
no. 121, Feb. 28, 1962, pp. 29, 35; Sale catalog, *Important
Modern Paintings, Drawings, Bronzes*, New York:
Parke-Bernet Galleries, Inc., Mar. 21, 1962, no. 80 repr.;
Arts, Mar. 1962, repr. p. 13; *Apollo*, Oct. 1965, repr. p. 338;
J. and H. Dauberville, *Bonnard, Catalogue Raisonné*, Paris:
Editions Bernheim-Jeune, 1968, vol. II, no. 528, repr.
p. 140; Sale catalog, *Highly Important 19th and 20th
Century Paintings, Drawings & Sculpture, from the Private
Collection of Norton Simon*, New York: Parke-Bernet
Galleries, Inc., May 5, 1971, no. 59, p. 114, repr. in color

Strongest as a colorist, weakest as a draftsman, Bonnard was
often at his best when a canvas of strongly marked shape
helped him structure his composition. In this picture the
rectangular shapes at the top and left side assist in giving
firmness, as do the value contrasts caused by the
backlighting of the figure. For the rest, Bonnard is free to
indulge the lavish richness of his purples, golds, and dark
greens. Consistently attracted to the timeless theme of the
bather, he has here used a languid pose recalling that of the
traditional *La Source*. The picture was said by Coquiot to
date from 1908 although the Daubervilles assign it to 1909.

40   Edouard Vuillard (1868-1940)
     In the Bus, ca. 1895
     Oil on board: 9¹³/₁₆″ x 9″ (25.0 x 22.9 cm.)
     Signed lower right: E. Vuillard

Collections: Georges Seligmann, New York; Dalzell Hatfield
Galleries, Los Angeles; Stephen Hahn Gallery, New York

Exhibitions: New York, Hammer Galleries, *40th
Anniversary Loan Exhibition, 1928-1968*, Nov. 7-Dec. 7,
1968 (repr. color in cat. p. 58); Memphis, Tennessee, Brooks
Memorial Art Gallery, *The Armand Hammer Collection*,
Oct. 2-Dec. 30, 1969, no. 63 (repr. in cat.); Washington,
D. C., Smithsonian Institution, *The Armand Hammer
Collection*, Mar. 20-May 17, 1970, no. 70 (repr. in cat. in

color); Smithsonian Institution Traveling Exhibition
Service, *The Armand Hammer Collection*, Kansas City,
Missouri, William Rockhill Nelson Gallery of Art, June
30-Aug. 2, 1970, New Orleans, Louisiana, Isaac Delgado
Museum of Art, Aug. 15-Sept. 20, 1970, Columbus, Ohio,
Columbus Gallery of Fine Arts, Oct. 9-Nov. 1, 1970, Little
Rock, Arkansas, Arkansas Art Center, Nov. 21, 1970-Jan.
12, 1971; San Francisco, California, California Palace of the
Legion of Honor, *The Armand Hammer Collection*, Feb.
11-Mar. 14, 1971; Oklahoma City, Oklahoma, Oklahoma
Art Center, *The Armand Hammer Collection*, June 15-July
11, 1971; San Diego, California, Fine Arts Gallery of San
Diego, *The Armand Hammer Collection*, July 23-Sept. 5,
1971

The *tachiste* paint application, which results in an all-over
decorative pattern, and the predominance of low-keyed
golden browns are characteristic of Vuillard at this date.
The subject of the painting is by no means clear.

41   Edouard Vuillard (1868-1940)
     Rue Lepic, Paris, 1908
     Tempera: 65″ x 18½″ (165.1 x 47.0 cm.)
     Signed lower right: E. Vuillard

Collections: Sam Salz, New York; Mr. and Mrs. Henry R.
Luce, New York

Exhibitions: Memphis, Tennessee, Brooks Memorial Art
Gallery, *The Armand Hammer Collection*, no. 65 (repr. in
cat.), Oct. 2-Dec. 30, 1969; Washington, D. C., Smithsonian
Institution, *The Armand Hammer Collection*, Mar. 20-May
17, 1970, no. 72 (repr. in cat. in color); Smithsonian
Institution Traveling Exhibition Service, *The Armand
Hammer Collection*, Kansas City, Missouri, William
Rockhill Nelson Gallery of Art, June 30-Aug. 2, 1970, New
Orleans, Louisiana, Isaac Delgado Museum of Art, Aug.
15-Sept. 20, 1970, Columbus, Ohio, Columbus Gallery of
Fine Arts, Oct. 9-Nov. 1, 1970, Little Rock, Arkansas,
Arkansas Art Center, Nov. 21, 1970-Jan. 12, 1971; San
Francisco, California, California Palace of the Legion of
Honor, *The Armand Hammer Collection*, Feb. 11-Mar. 14,
1971; Oklahoma City, Oklahoma, Oklahoma Art Center,
The Armand Hammer Collection, June 15-July 11, 1971;
San Diego, California, Fine Arts Gallery of San Diego, *The
Armand Hammer Collection*, July 23-Sept. 5, 1971

Literature: Claude Roger-Marx, *Vuillard et son Temps*,
Paris: Arts et Métiers Graphiques, 1945, p. 140 (original
project, with additional twelve inches of sky, reproduced
p. 161); John Russell, *Edouard Vuillard* (exhibition cat.),
Toronto: Art Gallery of Toronto, 1971, p. 232, no. 69,
repr. pl. 69

The tall, narrow format imposed by projects for decorative
screens or room panels seem to have been particularly
congenial to the Nabis. In this one the matte paint

application, leaving space for the support to show through, may evidence Vuillard's awareness of Toulouse-Lautrec. The composition, cut down by about a foot from its original dimensions, was one of a series of sketches of streets and squares of Paris for a projected room decoration for Henri Bernstein. Roger-Marx reproduces it in its original size next to a similar panel of a park in Paris. The Rue Lepic runs into the Place Blanche in Montmartre, the center of Nabi activity.

42 Edouard Vuillard (1868-1940)
At the Seashore, ca. 1904
Oil on panel: 8½" x 8½" (21.6 x 21.6 cm.)
Signed lower left: E. Vuillard

Collections: Joseph Hessel, Paris; Alfred Daber, Paris; Sam Salz, New York; Mr. and Mrs. Henry R. Luce, New York

Exhibitions: Paris, Musée du Louvre, Pavillon Marsan, *Vuillard*, 1938; Paris, Galerie Charpentier, *Vuillard*, 1946; New York, Museum of Modern Art, and Cleveland Museum of Art, *Edouard Vuillard, 1954* (cat. p. 103); Memphis, Tennessee, Brooks Memorial Art Gallery, *The Armand Hammer Collection*, Oct. 2-Dec. 30, 1969, no. 64 (repr. in cat.); Washington, D. C., Smithsonian Institution, *The Armand Hammer Collection*, Mar. 20-May 17, 1970, no. 71 (repr. in cat. in color); Smithsonian Institution Traveling Exhibition Service, *The Armand Hammer Collection*, Kansas City, Missouri, William Rockhill Nelson Gallery of Art, June 30-Aug. 2, 1970, New Orleans, Louisiana, Isaac Delgado Museum of Art, Aug. 15-Sept. 20, 1970, Columbus, Ohio, Columbus Gallery of Fine Arts, Oct. 9-Nov. 1, 1970, Little Rock, Arkansas, Arkansas Art Center, Nov. 21, 1970-Jan. 12, 1971; San Francisco, California, California Palace of the Legion of Honor, *The Armand Hammer Collection*, Feb. 11-Mar. 14, 1971; Oklahoma City, Oklahoma, Oklahoma Art Center, *The Armand Hammer Collection*, June 15-July 11, 1971; San Diego, California, Fine Arts Gallery of San Diego, *The Armand Hammer Collection*, July 23-Sept. 5, 1971; Toronto, Ontario, Art Gallery of Ontario, *Edouard Vuillard*, Sept. 11-Oct. 24, 1971, and San Francisco, California, Nov. 18, 1971-Jan. 2, 1972; Chicago, Illinois, Art Institute of Chicago, *Edouard Vuillard*, Jan. 28-Mar. 12, 1972, no. 59

Literature: Jacques Salomon, *Vuillard*, Paris: Gallimard, 1968, no. 100, as *Lucie Hessel devant la Mer*, repr. in color; François Daulte, "Hammer en dix chefs-d'oeuvre," *Connaissance des Arts*, no. 233, Sept. 1970, p. 85, repr. in color; John Russell, *Edouard Vuillard* (exhibition cat.), Toronto: Art Gallery of Ontario, 1971, p. 231, repr. pl. 59

"This little painting" wrote Jacques Salomon, "is like a cry from the heart, the echo of which ravished me when I admired it on Lucie Hessel's mantelpiece; the touch is so alive, so alert, so completely submissive to the rhythm of

Vuillard's feeling." Vuillard first met Mme. Hessel in 1900, and it was in her apartment in the Rue de Rivoli that he henceforth found most of his sitters, the most constant of these being Mme. Hessel herself. She was in Jacques Salomon's words "beautiful and elegant, without being pretty. Mme. Hessel joined great qualities of judgment and feeling to a real distinction. Vuillard devoted to her a constant friendship which for forty years was not troubled by the slightest cloud."

Lucie Hessel was the wife of Joseph Hessel, first director of the Galerie Bernheim-Jeune and later an important independent dealer in Rue La Boëtie.

43 Edouard Vuillard (1868-1940)
Interior, ca. 1910
Oil on board: 21⅛" x 15⅞" (53.3 x 40.3 cm.)
Stamped lower right: E. Vuillard (see Lugt 2497a)*

Collections: The Hanover Gallery, London; Edward Le Bas, Brighton (Sale, Geneva, Christie, Manson & Woods, Nov. 6, 1969, no. 164, repr.)

Exhibitions: London, Royal Academy, *A Painter's Collection* (Edward Le Bas Coll.), Mar. 19-Apr. 28, 1963, no. 120; Washington, D. C., Smithsonian Institution, *The Armand Hammer Collection*, Mar. 20-May 17, 1970, no. 73 (repr. in cat. in color); Smithsonian Institution Traveling Exhibition Service, *The Armand Hammer Collection*, Kansas City, Missouri, William Rockhill Nelson Gallery of Art, June 30-Aug. 2, 1970, New Orleans, Louisiana, Isaac Delgado Museum of Art, Aug. 15-Sept. 20, 1970, Columbus, Ohio, Columbus Gallery of Fine Arts, Oct. 9-Nov. 1, 1970, Little Rock, Arkansas, Arkansas Art Center, Nov. 21, 1970-Jan. 12, 1971; San Francisco, California, California Palace of the Legion of Honor, *The Armand Hammer Collection*, Feb. 11-Mar. 14, 1971; Oklahoma City, Oklahoma, Oklahoma Art Center, *The Armand Hammer Collection*, June 15-July 11, 1971; San Diego, California, Fine Arts Gallery of San Diego, *The Armand Hammer Collection*, July 23-Sept. 5, 1971

Literature: Sale catalog: *Impressionist and Modern Drawings, Paintings and Sculpture*, Geneva: Christie, Manson & Woods, Nov. 6, 1969, no. 164, repr.

Lighter in tone than is common for Vuillard, this airy composition is held together by the rectangular forms of the window, doorway, and chair, and by the strong vertical of the open door. Interiors without figures are rare for Vuillard. In this case, the scene may be that of his studio on the Boulevard Malsherbes.

*See Frits Lugt, *Les Marques de Collections, de Dessins & d'Estampes*, Le Haye 1956, Supplement, pp. 363-364. After Vuillard's death his sister and brother-in-law, M. & Mme. K-X Roussel, put stamps (E Vuillard or E V) on the works which remained in his studio as well as on a few which belonged to the family or to Vuillard's close friends.

44 André Derain (1880-1954)
Still Life with Basket, Jug and Fruit, 1911
Oil on canvas: 19⅞" x 23¹¹/₁₆" (50.5 x 60.1 cm.)
Signed lower right: a derain

Collections: Galerie Simon, Paris; Galerie Matthieson, Berlin; Edward Le Bas, Brighton

Exhibitions: London, C.E.M.A. Exhibition, *20th Century French Paintings and Drawings*, 1943, no. 10; London, Royal Academy, *A Painter's Collection* (Edward Le Bas Coll.), Mar. 19-Apr. 28, 1963, no. 10; Smithsonian Institution, *The Armand Hammer Collection*, Mar. 20-May 17, 1970, no. 87 (repr. in cat. in color); Smithsonian Institution Traveling Exhibition Service, *The Armand Hammer Collection*, Kansas City, Missouri, William Rockhill Nelson Gallery of Art, June 30-Aug. 2, 1970, New Orleans, Louisiana, Isaac Delgado Museum of Art, Aug. 15-Sept. 20, 1970, Columbus, Ohio, Columbus Gallery of Fine Arts, Oct. 9-Nov. 1, 1970, Little Rock, Arkansas, Arkansas Art Center, Nov. 21, 1970-Jan. 12, 1971; San Francisco, California, California Palace of the Legion of Honor, *The Armand Hammer Collection*, Feb. 11-Mar. 14, 1971; Oklahoma City, Oklahoma, Oklahoma Art Center, *The Armand Hammer Collection*, June 15-July 11, 1971; San Diego, California, Fine Arts Gallery of San Diego, *The Armand Hammer Collection*, July 23-Sept. 5, 1971

Literature: *L'Esprit Nouveau*, May 1921, repr.; Sale catalog, *Impressionist and Modern Drawings, Paintings and Sculpture*, Geneva: Christie, Manson & Woods, Nov. 6, 1969, no. 165, repr.

At the same time that he was painting more clearly Cubist-derived works, Derain was also working in the flatter, heavier style of this picture. One sees the influence of Cubism in the stylization of the shapes, the paint application of the background, and the restricted palette. The particular range of dark hues employed in this picture was favored by Derain throughout his career, and the style of this work is in every way more prophetic of his future than were many of the paintings executed at this time.

45 Amedeo Modigliani (1884-1920)
Woman of the People, 1918
Oil on canvas: 39¼" x 25⅝" (99.7 x 65.1 cm.)
Signed upper right: Modigliani

Collections: André Léfèvre, Paris; Blair Laing, Toronto, Canada; Dr. Armand Hammer, Los Angeles; Los Angeles County Museum of Art (Gift of Dr. and Mrs. Armand Hammer, 1968)

Exhibitions: Brussels, Palais des Beaux-Arts, *Modigliani*, 1933, no. 53; Paris, Petit Palais, *Les Maîtres de l'Art Indépendants, 1895-1937*, June-Oct. 1937, no. 77; Paris, Musée National d'Art Moderne, *L'Oeuvre du XXᵉ Siècle*, May-June 1952, no. 73; London, The Arts Council, *XXth Century Masterpieces*, 1952, no. 67; Paris, Musée National d'Art Moderne, *Collection André Léfèvre*, Mar.-Apr. 1964, no. 209; New York, Hammer Galleries, *40th Anniversary Loan Exhibition, 1928-1968*, Nov. 7-Dec. 7, 1968 (repr. color in cat. p. 39); Memphis, Tennessee, Brooks Memorial Art Gallery, *The Armand Hammer Collection*, Oct. 2-Dec. 30, 1969, no. 79 (repr. in cat.); Washington, D. C., Smithsonian Institution, *The Armand Hammer Collection*, Mar. 20-May 17, 1970, no. 89 (repr. color in cat.); Smithsonian Institution Traveling Exhibition Service, *The Armand Hammer Collection*, New Orleans, Louisiana, Isaac Delgado Museum of Art, Aug. 15-Sept. 20, 1970; San Francisco, California, California Palace of the Legion of Honor, *The Armand Hammer Collection*, Feb. 11-Mar. 14, 1971; San Diego, California, Fine Arts Gallery of San Diego, *The Armand Hammer Collection*, July 23-Sept. 5, 1971

Literature: Maurice Raynal, *Peintres du XXᵉ Siècle*, Geneva: 1947, repr. in color pl. 38; Maurice Raynal, *La Peinture Française Contemporaine*, Geneva: Skira, ca. 1960, repr. in color pl. 37 and on cover; *Modigliani*, New York: Skira Color Prints, n.d., pl. I; Claude Roy, *Modigliani*, Geneva: Skira, 1958 (The Taste of Our Time), p. 80, repr.; Sale catalog, *Vente Léfèvre*, Paris: Palais Galliéra, Nov. 25, 1965, repr.

This portrait of Germaine Lable, daughter of the concierge of the artist's close friend, the poet Max Jacob, was painted in 1918, two years before Modigliani's premature death at the age of thirty-six.

The painting exemplifies Modigliani's distinctive ability to capture the unique characterization of his sitter through, or one might almost say despite, his personal, elegantly mannered style of portraiture. The elongated oval face, drooping shoulder lines and pursed lips were all favorite devices of the artist. The delicately balanced facial features and the graceful curves of hairline, scarf, and drapery reveal the artist's masterful draftsmanship.

This commonplace woman of the people, seated in a basically static frontal position, is juxtaposed to the diagonal angle of the bed so that the curvilinear pattern of the head rail and pillow complement the curves in the figure and create a dynamic interplay of compositional forces. The combination of spatial flatness and subtle distortions of linear and shape relationships results in a unified, highly evocative composition; the abstract rhythm of formal elements across the pictorial surface alone carries the weight of the personal human content. It is precisely this way of conveying incisive portrait characterization with the most elegant and sparse formal means that makes Modigliani so moving and original an artist.

46 Maurice de Vlaminck (1876-1958)
Summer Bouquet
Oil on canvas: 25¾" x 21⁹/₁₆" (65.4 x 54.7 cm.)
Signed lower left: Vlaminck

Collections: James Vigeveno Galleries, Los Angeles; Mr. and Mrs. Henry R. Luce, New York

Exhibitions: Smithsonian Institution Traveling Exhibition Service, *The Armand Hammer Collection*, Kansas City, Missouri, William Rockhill Nelson Gallery of Art, June 30-Aug. 2, 1970, New Orleans, Louisiana, Isaac Delgado Museum of Art, Aug 15-Sept. 20, 1970, Columbus, Ohio, Columbus Gallery of Fine Arts, Oct. 9-Nov. 1, 1970, Little Rock, Arkansas, Arkansas Art Center, Nov. 21, 1970-Jan. 12, 1971; San Francisco, California, California Palace of the Legion of Honor, *The Armand Hammer Collection*, Feb. 11-Mar. 14, 1971; Oklahoma City, Oklahoma, Oklahoma Art Center, *The Armand Hammer Collection*, June 15-July 11, 1971; San Diego, California, Fine Arts Gallery of San Diego, *The Armand Hammer Collection*, July 23-Sept. 5, 1971

Vlaminck was so prolific as a landscape painter that his vases of flowers are comparatively rare. Yet he did, however, paint flower still lifes sporadically through most of his career. Of this rather late work, John Walker wrote in a manuscript note on the Hammer Collection: "His handling of the thick, juicy paint which is one of his most attractive talents is here beautifully displayed, especially in the petals of the flowers. De Stael never produced a more brilliant display of palette-knife virtuosity."

47 Georges Rouault (1871-1958)
Circus Girl, 1939
Oil on paper: 25¾" x 20¹¹/₁₆" (65.4 x 52.5 cm.)
Signed lower right. G. Rouault

Collections: Ambroise Vollard, Paris; Edwin C. Vogel, New York; Perls Gallery, New York; Vladimir Golschmann, St. Louis; Stephen Hahn Gallery, New York

Exhibitions: New York, Hammer Galleries, *40th Anniversary Loan Exhibition, 1928-1968*, Nov. 7-Dec. 7, 1968 (repr. color in cat. p. 49); Memphis, Tennessee, Brooks Memorial Art Gallery, *The Armand Hammer Collection*, Oct. 2-Dec. 30, 1969, no. 69 (repr. in cat.); Washington, D. C., Smithsonian Institution, *The Armand Hammer Collection*, Mar. 20-May 17, 1970, no. 77 (repr. in cat. in color); Smithsonian Institution Traveling Exhibition Service, *The Armand Hammer Collection*, Kansas City, Missouri, William Rockhill Nelson Gallery of Art, June 30-Aug. 2, 1970, New Orleans, Louisiana, Isaac Delgado Museum of Art, Aug. 15-Sept. 20, 1970, Columbus, Ohio, Columbus Gallery of Fine Arts, Oct. 9-Nov. 1, 1970, Little Rock, Arkansas, Arkansas Art Center, Nov. 21, 1970-Jan. 12, 1971; San Francisco, California, California Palace of the Legion of Honor, *The Armand Hammer Collection*, Feb. 11-Mar. 14, 1971; Oklahoma City, Oklahoma, Oklahoma Art Center, *The Armand Hammer Collection*, June 15-July 11, 1971

It is possible to see in Rouault's heavily-impastoed and stained-glass-like style a reflection of the bejeweled richness of the style of his master Gustave Moreau. Both Rouault's style and his subjects, of which the circus was one, altered little throughout his career. In 1938, approximately the date of this picture, he completed a series of seven etchings and eighty-two wood engravings for André Suarès' *Le Cirque*. There are at least four other pictures with the same subject and title as this (Courthion 305, 307, 310, Glasgow).

48 Kees van Dongen (1877-1968)
Friends, 1908
Oil on canvas: 39⅜" x 31⅞" (100.0 x 80.9 cm.)
Signed lower right: van Dongen
Inscription on reverse: "Amies, Kees van Dongen, Paris, 35 rue Lamarck" (van Dongen moved to 35 rue Lamarck in 1908, then to 6 rue Saulnier in 1909)

Collection: Ludwig Bemelmans, New York

Exhibitions: Memphis, Tennessee, Brooks Memorial Art Gallery, *The Armand Hammer Collection*, Oct. 2-Dec. 30, 1969, no. 76 (repr. in cat.); Washington, D. C., Smithsonian Institution, *The Armand Hammer Collection*, Mar. 20-May 17, 1970, no. 84 (repr. in cat. in color); Smithsonian Institution Traveling Exhibition Service, *The Armand Hammer Collection*, Kansas City, Missouri, William Rockhill Nelson Gallery of Art, June 30-Aug. 2, 1970, New Orleans, Louisiana, Isaac Delgado Museum of Art, Aug. 15-Sept. 20, 1970, Columbus, Ohio, Columbus Gallery of Fine Arts, Oct. 9-Nov. 1, 1970, Little Rock, Arkansas, Arkansas Art Center, Nov. 21, 1970-Jan. 12, 1971; San Francisco, California, California Palace of the Legion of Honor, *The Armand Hammer Collection*, Feb. 11-Mar. 14, 1971; Oklahoma City, Oklahoma, Oklahoma Art Center, *The Armand Hammer Collection*, June 15-July 11, 1971

Kees van Dongen is so well known for his chic stylizations of fashionable society it is often forgotten that he was a major link between French Fauvism and German Expressionism. Van Dongen came to Paris from Rotterdam in 1897, and by 1905 he was exhibiting with Matisse, Vlaminck, Derain, and Rouault, having adopted the pure color and bold lines of his Fauve colleagues. When Pechstein returned to Germany from Paris in 1908 after a brief visit, it was van Dongen not Matisse whom he invited to exhibit with the "Brucke" group. The *Friends* of 1908-09 with its significative formal distortion and psychological concern is, indeed, structurally closer to Kirchner and Heckel than to the Fauve delight in aesthetic experience.

49 Marie Laurencin (1885-1956)
Women in the Forest
Oil on canvas: 31⅞" x 39⅝" (81.0 x 107.0 cm.)
Signed and dated lower right: Marie Laurencin 1920

Collections: Paul Rosenberg, Paris; John Quinn, New York;
Forrestal, New York; Martin Horrell, New York; Leo
Aarons, New York; Stephen Hahn Gallery, New York

Exhibitions: New York, Art Center, *Memorial Exhibition of
the John Quinn Collection*, Jan. 8-30, 1926; Memphis,
Tennesseee, Brooks Memorial Art Gallery, *The Armand
Hammer Collection*, Oct .2-Dec. 30, 1969, no. 80 (repr. in
cat.); Washington, D. C., Smithsonian Institution, *The
Armand Hammer Collection*, Mar. 20-May 17, 1970; no. 90
(repr. in cat. in color); Smithsonian Institution Traveling
Exhibition Service, *The Armand Hammer Collection*, Kansas
City, Missouri, William Rockhill Nelson Gallery of Art,
June 30-Aug. 2, 1970, New Orleans, Louisiana, Isaac
Delgado Museum of Art, Aug. 15-Sept. 20, 1970, Columbus,
Ohio, Columbus Gallery of Fine Arts, Oct. 9-Nov. 1, 1970,
Little Rock, Arkansas, Arkansas Art Center, Nov. 21,
1970-Jan. 12, 1971; San Francisco, California, California
Palace of the Legion of Honor, *The Armand Hammer
Collection*, Feb. 11-Mar. 14, 1971; Oklahoma City,
Oklahoma, Oklahoma Art Center, *The Armand Hammer
Collection*, June 15-July 11, 1971

Literature: Roger Allard, *Marie Laurencin* (Les Peintres
Français Nouveaux, no. 9), Paris: Gallimard, 1921, repr.
p. 49; Forbes Watson, *John Quinn 1870-1925, Collection of
Paintings, Water Colors, Drawings & Sculpture*,
Huntington, New York: Pidgeon Hill Press, 1926, p. 11,
repr. p. 66; B. L. Reid, *The Man from New York*, New York:
1968, pp. 470-471

Marie Laurencin was closely associated with the Cubists
before World War I and with the artists who formed Cubist
splinter movements after the War, but her style was little
affected by any of them. Guillaume Apollinaire
characterized her painting in *The Cubist Painters*: "Like the
dance, it is an infinitely gracious and rhythmical art of
enumeration." Her iconography of sylph-like girls and
gentle animals in an Arcadian landscape is a personal lyric
invention—suggestive rather than literal. This large work,
Women in the Forest, seems to be a monumental restatement
of elements Laurencin had used in numerous small paintings
between 1917 and 1920.

50 Marc Chagall (1887-   )
Blue Angel
Gouache and pastel: 20" x 26" (50.8 x 66.1 cm.)

Collections: Frank Crowninshield, New York; Mr. and Mrs.
Henry R. Luce, New York

Exhibitions: New York, Galerie Chalette, 1958; Tokyo,

National Museum of Art, Oct. 1-Nov. 10, 1963; Kyoto,
National Art Gallery of Kyoto, Nov. 20-Dec. 10, 1963;
Memphis, Tennessee, Brooks Memorial Art Gallery, *The
Armand Hammer Collection*, Oct. 2-Dec. 30, 1969, no. 82
(repr. in cat.); Washington, D. C., Smithsonian Institution,
The Armand Hammer Collection, Mar. 20-May 17, 1970, no.
92 (repr. in cat. in color); Smithsonian Institution Traveling
Exhibition Service, *The Armand Hammer Collection*,
Kansas City, Missouri, William Rockhill Nelson Gallery of
Art, June 30-Aug. 2, 1970, New Orleans, Louisiana, Isaac
Delgado Museum of Art, Aug. 15-Sept. 20, 1970, Columbus,
Ohio, Columbus Gallery of Fine Arts, Oct. 9-Nov. 1, 1970,
Little Rock, Arkansas, Arkansas Art Center, Nov. 21,
1970-Jan. 12, 1971; San Francisco, California, California
Palace of the Legion of Honor, *The Armand Hammer
Collection*, Feb. 11-Mar. 14, 1971; Oklahoma City,
Oklahoma, Oklahoma Art Center, *The Armand Hammer
Collection*, June 15-July 11, 1971

Literature: Franz Meyer, *Marc Chagall, Life and Work*,
New York: Harry N. Abrams, Inc., 1964, no. 672,
repr., p. 757

The theatrical blue-red color harmony of this work and its
juxtaposition of normally unrelated figures, floating and
dream-like, are typical of Chagall. Although the angel may
have been particularly in Chagall's mind because of the
illustrations for the Bible he had been commissioned by
Vollard to do in the early 1930s, both it and the bouquet
of flowers are common in his scenes of lovers and
newly-weds. Franz Meyer suggests that the "new natural
sensuousness" of the pictures of 1937-1939 was the result
of the increased security in Chagall's personal affairs
during that time.

51 Gilbert Stuart (1755-1828)
Portrait of George Washington, 1822
Oil on canvas: 44⅛" x 34½" (112.0 x 87.6 cm.)

Collections: William D. Lewis, Philadelphia; Estate of
William D. Lewis (on loan to Pennsylvania Academy of the
Fine Arts, Philadelphia, 1881-1928); Howard Young
Galleries, New York; Mr. and Mrs. Alfred G. Wilson,
Detroit (Sale, New York: Parke-Bernet Galleries, Inc., Dec.
10, 1970, no. 12)

Exhibitions: The Detroit Institute of Arts, *The Eleventh
Loan Exhibition, American Colonial and Early Federal Art*,
Feb. 4-Mar. 2, 1930, no. 81; The Detroit Institute of Arts,
Masterpieces of Painting from Detroit Private Collections,
Apr. 23-May 22, 1949, no. 30 (lent by Mr. and Mrs. Alfred
G. Wilson in 1930 and 1949); Smithsonian Institution
Traveling Exhibition Service, *The Armand Hammer
Collection*, Little Rock, Arkansas, Arkansas Art Center, Nov.
21,1970-Jan. 12, 1971; San Francisco, California, California
Palace of the Legion of Honor, *The Armand Hammer
Collection*, Feb. 11-Mar. 14, 1971; Oklahoma City,

Oklahoma, Oklahoma Art Center, *The Armand Hammer Collection*, June 15-July 11, 1971

Literature: Henry T. Tuckerman, *Book of Artists*, New York: G. P. Putnam & Son, 1867, p. 120; George C. Mason, *Life and Works of Gilbert Stuart*, New York: Charles Scribner's Sons, 1879, p. 113; Elizabeth Bryant Johnston, *Original Portraits of Washington*, Boston: James R. Osgood & Co., 1882, pp. 81, 82; Mantle Fielding, *Gilbert Stuart's Portraits of Washington*, Philadelphia: 1923, no. 30, p. 148; Lawrence Park, *Gilbert Stuart, An Illustrated Descriptive List of His Works*, New York: William Edwin Rudge, 1926, vol. II, no. 31, p. 862; John Hill Morgan and Mantle Fielding, *The Life Portraits of Washington and Their Replicas*, Philadelphia: Lancaster Press, Inc., 1931, no. 31, p. 271; G. A. Eisen, *Portraits of Washington*, New York: Robert Hamilton & Associates, 1932, p. 126, repr. p. 255; Sale catalog, *Important American Paintings, Sculpture and Drawings*, New York: Parke-Bernet Galleries, Inc., Dec. 10, 1970, no. 12, p. 14, repr. in color

Whatever Stuart's reasons for leaving Ireland in 1793, he returned to this country expecting to capitalize on the demand for portraits of George Washington. It was an astute and logical move for one of the greatest portrait painters of the period. Such was the stature of Washington, already the personification of the nation, that Stuart and his competitors, the Peales, found it profitable to devote a great part of their energy and time to recording his image.

Sittings in 1795 resulted in the "Vaughan" type of bust portrait, and in 1796 the President sat for the famous "Athenaeum" portrait now in the Boston Museum. When Senator William Bingham asked for a full-length portrait in 1796, the "Athenaeum" portrait was used as the model for the head in the composition which became known as the "Landsdowne" type. The present half-length, painted for William D. Lewis in 1822, is based on the "Lansdowne" full length, specifically on the later version now in the New York Public Library (Lenox Collection) painted at the request of Peter Jay Munro. The basic composition is that of the Constable-Hamilton half-length of 1797, also in the New York Public Library.

52 William Michael Harnett (1848-1892)
Still Life, 1885
Oil on panel: 13¾" x 10⁵/₁₆" (34.9 x 26.2 cm.)
Signed and dated lower left: WM Harnett 1885

Collections: George Richmond, London (Studio Sale, Christie, Manson & Woods, May 1, 1897, no. 4); Lord Justice William Rann Kennedy (Sale, London, Christie, Manson & Woods, Feb. 19, 1971, no. 177)

Exhibitions: London, Royal Academy of Arts, May 1885, no. 860 (purchased by George Richmond); St. Helens, Victoria Park, *First Summer Exhibition*, 1892, no. 105;

Oklahoma City, Oklahoma, Oklahoma Art Center, *The Armand Hammer Collection*, June 15-July 11, 1971; San Diego, California, Fine Arts Gallery of San Diego, *The Armand Hammer Collection*, July 23-Sept. 5, 1971

Literature: Algernon Graves, *The Royal Academy of Arts, A Complete Dictionary of Contributors and Their Work from Its Foundation in 1769 to 1904*, London: Henry Graves & Co., Ltd. and George Bell & Sons, 1905, no. 860, p. 395; *Magazine of Art*, Feb. 1951, p. 66; Alfred Frankenstein, *After the Hunt, William Harnett and Other American Still Life Painters*, Berkeley and Los Angeles: University of California Press, 1953, pp. 70, 71, and rev. ed., 1969, pp. 70, 71; Sale catalog, *Pictures, Drawings, Bronzes and Prints of American, Australian, Canadian, New Zealand and South African Interest*, London: Christie, Manson & Woods, Feb. 19, 1971, no. 177, p. 49, repr. opp. in color

Though Harnett's *trompe-l'oeil* painting has a counterpart in the history of European art, it stands as a culmination of the long tradition of American Realism. Five years abroad had an effect on Harnett's work but did not erase the unique, personal elements of his style nor the stamp of forthright vision which characterizes so much of American painting.

Painted in Paris in 1885, this *Still Life* was sent to the Royal Academy in London where it was noted in the *Times* as "... one of the most miraculous representations ... that we have ever seen." The writer undoubtedly was referring to the degree of realism of the painting. For, while the arrangement of solid objects in Harnett's *Still Life* does not permit the kind of visual deception typical of the more two-dimensional rack paintings in which flat objects such as cards and envelopes are mounted on a board, it nevertheless achieves an almost tangible extension into space. But Harnett achieves more than an illusion of three-dimensionality. In this work Harnett displays his particular genius in the highly sophisticated balance of color, form, and texture. Even the subtle shifts in hue among the variously faded sheets of music are exploited to the fullest, and the qualities of paper, metal, leather, velvet, and wood are explored and juxtaposed so as to play the full visual scale.

Another almost identical painting at Yale University has been mistaken for this one which was bought by George Richmond from the Royal Academy in 1885. The only obvious difference between the two, probably introduced to avoid exactly the kind of problem which has arisen, is the reversal of the printed word fragments on the roll of music protruding at the left and again on the top sheet of music at the front edge of the cabinet. Apparently Harnett himself was a victim of this confusion, for, on the back of a photograph—owned by Alfred Frankenstein—of the Yale painting, an inscription in the artist's own hand identifies it as the George Richmond still life.

53 John Singer Sargent (1856-1925)
Doctor Pozzi at Home, 1881
Oil on canvas: 80½" x 43⅞" (204.5 x 111.5 cm.)
Signed and dated upper right: John S. Sargent, 1881

Collection: Estate of the Hon. Jean Pozzi (Sale, Paris, Palais Galliéra, Dec. 4, 1970, no. 84, repr., also on cat. cover in color)

Exhibitions: San Francisco, California, California Palace of the Legion of Honor, *The Armand Hammer Collection*, Feb. 11-Mar. 14, 1971; Oklahoma City, Oklahoma, Oklahoma Art Center, *The Armand Hammer Collection*, June 15-July 11, 1971; San Diego, California, Fine Arts Gallery of San Diego, *The Armand Hammer Collection*, July 23-Sept. 5, 1971

Literature: *L'Art et les Artistes*, vol. IV (1905-1907), p. 368, repr.; William Howe Downes, *John S. Sargent, His Life and Work*, Boston: Little, Brown, & Company, 1925, pp. 10-11, 113; Hon. Evan Charteris, *John Sargent*, New York: Charles Scribner's Sons, 1927, p. 258; Charles Merrill Mount, *John Singer Sargent*, London: The Cresset Press, 1957, pp. 61, 65, 67, 69, 116, 153; Richard Ormond, *John Singer Sargent, Paintings, Drawings, Watercolors*, New York: Harper & Row, 1970, p. 34; Sale catalog, *Tableaux Modernes, Sculptures*, Paris: Palais Galliéra, Dec. 4, 1970, no. 84, repr., also on cat. cover in color

While there was still a decidedly youthful quality in Sargent's work in 1881, he was rapidly reaching full stride as an artist. Already honored in the Salon of 1879 for the dramatic portrait of his teacher, Carolus-Duran, in 1881 he received a medal second class, making him "*. . . hors concours* and a great swell," as he jokingly put it. The portrait of *Dr. Pozzi at Home* was eagerly undertaken by an artist brimming with enthusiasm and confidence.

Innovative from the beginning, Sargent was never content with a formal, straightforward likeness. Even in the early portrait of Carolus, the teacher assumes a special vitality in a dynamic pose conveying force and movement. It was perhaps the influence of Impressionism that led him to ask Mme. Pailleron to pose standing out of doors when he painted the full-length standing portrait which appeared in the Salon of 1880. Some of his greatest portraits are the most informal ones, catching the subject engaged in life, as it were; the portrait of Dr. Pozzi is a powerful statement of this kind. Moving beyond the snapshot effect which could so easily result from this approach, the artist brings to the painting much more than the experience of Carolus' studio. Certainly, the solid grasp of form and light, particularly in the head, reflects the method of his teacher, but Sargent's own personal gift, expanded and refined by a close study of the old masters, is affirmed. The drama of the painting is an extension of the artist's response to the work of Velàsquez and Hals which he had studied so closely in previous months. In gesture and movement the figure is purely Baroque, and, despite the overt drama of the technically superb glazes, there is a subtlety of light and tone which could have had its source in Velàsquez.

54 John Singer Sargent (1856-1925)
Portrait of Mrs. Edward L. Davis and Her Son, Livingston Davis, 1890
Oil on canvas: 86" x 48" (218.4 x 121.9 cm.)
Signed lower right: John S. Sargent

Collections: Edward Livingston Davis, Worcester, Mass.; Livingston Davis, Boston, Mass.; Mrs. A. Winsor Weld, Boston, Mass. (Sale, New York, Parke-Bernet Galleries, Inc., Mar. 19-20, 1969, no. 74); James Graham & Sons, New York; Los Angeles County Museum of Art, Los Angeles, Calif. (Frances and Armand Hammer Purchase Fund, 1969)

Exhibitions: New York, National Academy of Design, 1890; New York, Society of American Artists, 1891; Boston, Boston Art Museum, 1891; Chicago, *World's Columbian Exhibition*, 1893, no. 875; Boston, Copley Hall, *Loan Collection of Portraits of Women*, 1895, no. 257; Philadelphia, Pennsylvania Academy of the Fine Arts, 1896; Boston, Copley Hall, *Paintings and Sketches by John S. Sargent, R. A.*, Feb. 20-Mar. 13, 1899, no. 5; Worcester, Mass., Worcester Art Museum, 1909; Boston, Museum of Fine Arts: 1913, no. 757; 1916, no. 573; 1918, no. 480; 1920, no. 340; 1921, no. 420; New York, Grand Central Art Galleries, *Retrospective Exhibition of Important Works of John Singer Sargent*, Feb. 23-Apr. 6, 1924, no. 20 (repr. in cat. p. 45); New York, The Metropolitan Museum of Art, *Memorial Exhibition of the Works of John Singer Sargent*, Jan. 4-Feb. 14, 1926, no. 26 (repr. in cat.); Boston, Museum of Fine Arts: 1928, no. 168; 1929, no. 993; 1930, no. 530; 1956, no. 20; Boston, Museum of Fine Arts, Centennial Exhibition, *Sargent's Boston*, Jan. 3-Feb. 7, 1956; Memphis, Tennessee, Brooks Memorial Art Gallery, *The Armand Hammer Collection*, Oct. 2-Dec. 30, 1969, no. 57 (repr. in cat.); Washington, D. C., Smithsonian Institution, *The Armand Hammer Collection*, Mar. 20-May 17, 1970, no. 63 (repr. in cat. in color); San Francisco, California, California Palace of the Legion of Honor, *The Armand Hammer Collection*, Feb. 11-Mar. 14, 1971

Literature: Leila Mechlin, "The Sargent Exhibition," *The American Magazine of Art*, vol. XV, no. 4, Apr. 1924, pp. 169-190, repr. p. 184; Rose V. S. Berry, "John Singer Sargent: Some of His American Work," *Art and Archaeology throughout the Ages*, vol. XVIII, no. 3, Sept. 1924, pp. 83-112, repr. p. 100; William Howe Downes, *John S. Sargent, His Life and Work*, Boston: Little, Brown & Co., 1925, pp. 33, 157-158, repr. p. 128; Evan Charteris, *John Sargent*, New York: Charles Scribner's Sons, 1927, pp. 109, 137, 263; Charles Merrill Mount, *John Singer*

Sargent, New York: W. W. Norton, 1955, pp. 183, 433, no. 9024; David McKibbin, *Sargent's Boston*, Boston: Museum of Fine Arts, 1956, pp. 43, 68, 91, repr. p. 41; Sale catalog, *18th-20th Century American Paintings, etc. —Various Owners*, New York: Parke-Bernet Galleries, Mar. 19-20, 1969, no. 74, repr.; Richard Ormond, *John Singer Sargent, Paintings, Drawings, Watercolors*, New York: Harper & Row, 1970, pp. 43, 246, repr.

By 1889 when Sargent came to this country to discuss the mural project for the Boston Public Library, he was already the most renowned portrait painter of his day. When he was not actually involved with plans for the murals, portrait commissions in New York and Boston kept him completely absorbed. It is typical of the artist that moving about from one country to another and from one city to the next did not interfere with his work nor impair its quality.

The portrait of *Mrs. Edward L. Davis and her Son, Livingston Davis*, painted, according to Downes, in the family's coach house, is not a simple bust portrait but an imposing composition demanding the artist's full powers of invention and execution. For Sargent the inherent challenge becomes inspiration, and the figures of the full-length, double portrait spring to life almost spontaneously.

The seemingly casual relationship between the two figures is actually a relationship of considerable formal and psychological complexity. The precarious movement of the boy is played against the monumentally stable form of his mother who looms forward as she forcefully confronts the viewer. While the broad, loose brushwork continues to reflect Sargent's debt to the Dutch and Spanish masters and even to an extent to the Impressionists, the firm modeling and dramatic lighting of the woman's head seem to have something of the quality of the realist Copley whose work Sargent discovered in Boston.

55 Thomas W. Eakins (1844-1916)
Portrait of Sebastiano Cardinal Martinelli, 1902
Oil on canvas, mounted on panel
78⁵⁄₁₆" x 59¹⁵⁄₁₆" (198.9 x 152.3 cm.)
Signed lower right: Eakins 1902
Inscribed on verso: EFFIGIES SEBASTIANI S R E CARDINALIS MARTINELLI QVI ANNOS VI IN STAT FOED AB MDCCCXCVI AD MCMII DELEGATI APOSTOLICI OFFICIO FVNTVS; below: THOS. EAKINS PHILADELPHIEN A.D. MCMII PINXIT
(Presently covered by panel)

Collection: The Catholic University of America, Washington, D. C. (presented by the artist in 1903) (Sale, New York, Parke-Bernet Galleries, Inc., May 21, 1970, no. 57, repr.)

Exhibitions: Pittsburgh, Museum of Art, Carnegie Institute, *International Exhibition*, 1903;* Philadelphia,

Institute, *International Exhibition*, 1903; Philadelphia, Pennsylvania Academy of the Fine Arts, *Thomas Eakins Memorial Exhibition*, Dec. 23, 1917—Jan. 23, 1918, no. 20; Baltimore Museum of Art, *Thomas Eakins, A Retrospective Exhibition of His Paintings*, Dec. 1, 1936-Jan. 1, 1937, no. 34; Philadelphia Museum of Art, *Thomas Eakins Centennial Exhibition*, 1944, no. 99; Pittsburgh, Museum of Art, Carnegie Institute, *Thomas Eakins Centennial Exhibition*, Apr. 26-June 1, 1945, no. 15, repr.; Washington, D. C., National Gallery of Art, 1969-1970; Overbrook, Pa., St. Charles Seminary, *Eakins Portraits*, 1970; Smithsonian Institution Traveling Exhibition Service, *The Armand Hammer Collection*, no. 101 (repr. in color on cover of cat. supplement), Kansas City, Missouri, William Rockhill Nelson Gallery of Art, June 30-Aug. 2, 1970, New Orleans, Louisiana, Isaac Delgado Museum of Art, Aug. 15-Sept. 20, 1970; New York, Whitney Museum of American Art, *Thomas Eakins Retrospective*, Sept. 21-Nov. 29, 1970; Little Rock, Arkansas, Arkansas Art Center, Dec. 11, 1970-Jan. 12, 1971; San Francisco, California, California Palace of the Legion of Honor, *The Armand Hammer Collection*, Feb. 11-Mar. 14, 1971; Oklahoma City, Oklahoma, Oklahoma Art Center, *The Armand Hammer Collection*, June 15-July 11, 1971; San Diego, California, Fine Arts Gallery of San Diego, *The Armand Hammer Collection*, July 23-Sept. 5, 1971

Literature: Lloyd Goodrich, *Thomas Eakins—His Life and Work*, New York: MacMillan Co., 1933, no. 361, pp. 105-106, 194; Fairfield Porter, *Thomas Eakins*, New York: George Braziller, Inc., 1959, repr. fig. 64; Sylvan Schendler, *Thomas Eakins*, Boston; Little, Brown & Co., 1967, pp. 201, 208, 215, 296, pl. 102; Sale catalog, *18th, 19th and 20th Century American Paintings*, New York: Parke-Bernet Galleries, Inc., May 21, 1970, no. 57, p. 58, repr. opp. in color

As Lloyd Goodrich has pointed out, it seems paradoxical that Thomas Eakins, a Quaker and an uncompromising realist, should have begun in his late years a series of portraits of Catholic prelates. Seen as portraits of friends painted at the artist's own request, however, they begin to take their place very logically within his total oeuvre. Rejected as an artist and rather withdrawn from society, Eakins must have felt a close kinship with these learned men whose mission set them apart from the world.

In the portrait of Cardinal Martinelli, Eakins has achieved a perfect balance between the human quality of the individual and the austerity of holy office. As is often the case in Eakins' full-length portraits, this figure is placed at some distance from the viewer within a very real space, and the ambience eloquently conveys a feeling of solitary contemplation. This effect is further enhanced by the use of the profile view which presents the figure as a hieratic image to be beheld without direct involvement of the spectator. From the casually rubbed earth color suggesting

wood paneling and parquet floor, to the subtle design of
the rug, more or less monochromatic surroundings act as a
foil, intensifying the impact of the Cardinal's presence.

*On September 16, 1903, Eakins wrote from 1729 Mt.
Vernon Street, Philadelphia, to the Rector of The Catholic
University of America:

> Dear Sir:
> I am the person who painted and presented to the
> University the full length portrait of Cardinal Martinelli.
> I am solicited by the Carnegie Institute to exhibit
> specimens of my best work, and I should like to send there
> the Cardinal which has been exhibited in New York,
> Philadelphia and Chicago.
> As the Carnegie Institute of Pittsburgh is absolutely
> fireproof I have no fear.
> It will be boxed and transported by agents of the
> Institute and insured for any value you may set upon it.
> The exhibition of the Carnegie lasts from Nov. 5
> to Jan. 1.
> Please let me know promptly if the picture may be
> exhibited.
>
> Yours truly,
> Thomas Eakins

56 Mary Cassatt (1844-1926)
Reine Lefebvre and Margot, ca. 1902
Pastel on brown paper, mounted on canvas:
32¾" x 26⁹/₁₆" (83.2 x 67.5 cm.)
Signed lower left: Mary Cassatt

Collections: Felix Doistau, Paris (Sale, Galerie Georges Petit,
June 18, 19, 1928, no. 6); Durand-Ruel, Paris and New York,
1929; Mrs. A. L. Adams (Sale, New York, Parke-Bernet
Galleries, Inc., Oct. 15, 1969, no. 16)

Exhibitions: New York, Durand-Ruel Galleries, *Mary
Cassatt*, Apr. 8-20, 1929, no. 1; Washington, D. C.,
Smithsonian Institution, *The Armand Hammer Collection*,
Mar. 20-May 17, 1970, no. 56 (repr. in cat. in color);
Smithsonian Institution Traveling Exhibition Service,
The Armand Hammer Collection, Kansas City, Missouri,
William Rockhill Nelson Gallery of Art, June 30-Aug. 2,
1970, New Orleans, Louisiana, Isaac Delgado Museum of
Art, Aug. 15-Sept. 20, 1970; Washington, D. C., National
Gallery of Art, *Mary Cassatt*, Sept. 27-Nov. 8, 1970, no. 70;
Little Rock, Arkansas, Arkansas Art Center, *The Armand
Hammer Collection*, Nov. 21, 1970-Jan. 12, 1971; San
Francisco, California, California Palace of the Legion of
Honor, *The Armand Hammer Collection*, Feb 11-Mar. 14,
1971; Oklahoma City, Oklahoma, Oklahoma Art Center,
The Armand Hammer Collection, June 15-July 11, 1971; San
Diego, California, Fine Arts Gallery of San Diego,
The Armand Hammer Collection, July 23- Sept. 5, 1971

Literature: *Revue de l'Art*, Nov. 1928; *Bulletin de l'Art
Ancien et Moderne*, Nov. 1928, vol. 54, p. 357, repr.; Adelyn
D. Breeskin, *Mary Cassatt, A Catalogue Raisonné of the
Oils, Pastels, Watercolors and Drawings*, Washington,
D. C.: Smithsonian Institution Press, 1970, no. 430, p. 170,

repr.; Sale catalog, *Important Impressionist and Modern
Paintings and Sculpture*, New York: Parke-Bernet Galleries,
Inc., Oct. 15, 1969, no. 16, repr. in color

Reine Lefebvre, a neighbor living in the village near Mary
Cassatt's Château de Beaufresne, posed for the artist, at
times along with the child Margot, from 1901 to 1903.
Though only sixteen and seventeen years old during this
association, she is imbued in this painting with a quiet
dignity and conveys a very convincing maternal relationship
with the child. Typical of Cassatt's pastels of this period,
the present work almost disguises the powerful
draftsmanship which won her the admiration of Degas.
The free and forceful strokes seem to activate the surface
in an almost random way, but ultimately the strength of
line emerges in the firm design.

57 Mary Cassatt (1844-1926)
Summertime, 1894
Oil on canvas: 28⅞" x 39⅜" (73.4 x 100.0 cm.)
Signed lower right: Mary Cassatt

Collection: Huntington Hartford, New York (Sale, New
York, Parke-Bernet Galleries, Inc., May 10, 1971, no. 28)

Exhibitions: Baltimore Museum of Art, *Manet, Degas,
Berthe Morisot and Mary Cassatt*, Apr. 18-June 3, 1962,
no. 116 (lent by Huntington Hartford); St. Petersburg,
Florida, Museum of Fine Arts, *Inaugural Exhibition*, Feb.
7-Mar. 7, 1965, no. 28 (lent by Huntington Hartford); New
York, M. Knoedler & Co., *Mary Cassatt*, Feb. 1-26, 1966,
no. 25 (lent by Huntington Hartford); Southampton, Long
Island, The Parrish Art Museum, *Miss Mary Cassatt,
Paintings and the Graphic Arts*, July 30-Aug. 20, 1967,
no. 2 (lent by Huntington Hartford); Washington, D. C.,
National Gallery of Art, *Mary Cassatt*, Sept. 27-Nov. 8,
1970, no. 55, p. 28 (repr. in cat.) (lent by Huntington
Hartford); Oklahoma City, Oklahoma, Oklahoma
Art Center, *The Armand Hammer Collection*, June 15-
July 11, 1971; San Diego, California, Fine Arts Gallery
of San Diego, *The Armand Hammer Collection*,
July 23-Sept. 5, 1971

Literature: Adelyn Dohme Breeskin, *Mary Cassatt, A
Catalogue Raisonné of the Oils, Pastels, Watercolors and
Drawings*, Washington, D. C.: Smithsonian Institution
Press, 1970, no. 240, p. 116, repr.; Meryle Secrest, "The
American Impressionist, the Lyrical Mary Cassatt Goes on
Exhibit in Washington," *The Washington Post*, Sept. 20,
1970, Section KI, repr. in color; Sale catalog, *Important
Impressionist and Modern Paintings and Drawings*, New
York: Parke-Bernet Galleries, Inc., May 10, 1971, no. 28,
p. 50, repr. in color

Though Mary Cassatt's paintings are generally more or less
complex figure compositions, she remains essentially a
portrait painter concentrating on the likeness and character

of individuals. As a rule even when she painted figures engaged in some activity out of doors, she remained as much concerned with portraiture as with the disposition of form and features within a pictorial space. Among the few exceptions are three boating scenes from 1893-1894 (Breeskin 230, 233, and 240.) In none of these are the subjects identified, but in the famous *The Boating Party (Near Antibes)*, 1893, the personalities emerge with great strength. In the other two, which are closely related, the identity of the figures is not an important factor, and the intention seems to be simply the creation of a plein-air view of figures in a boat observing or feeding ducks.

A number of important factors entered into the conception of *Summertime*. As early as 1890 Cassatt had resolved to concentrate on strengthening form and drawing, much as Renoir did in mid-career, and the following year a series of prints emulating the Japanese had a profound effect on her style. This is obvious in *The Boating Party*, but while boldness of design is still very important in *Summertime*, it is augmented by a system of slashing, dynamic brushwork verging on abstraction. Interestingly, the large allegory commissioned for the Chicago World's Fair and painted in 1892 also included women and ducks in a landscape.

58 Maurice Brazil Prendergast (1861-1924)
On the Beach, 1916
Oil on canvas: 26¾" x 39" (67.9 x 99.0 cm.)

Collections: Mrs. Charles Prendergast, Westport, Conn.; Lester Avnet, New York; A.C.A. Galleries, New York

Exhibitions: Pittsburgh, Penna., Museum of Art, Carnegie Institute, *The 23rd Annual International Exhibition of Paintings*, April 24-June 15, 1924, no. 14; Hartford, Conn., Wadsworth Atheneum, *Connecticut Collections*, Oct., 1957; Stamford, Conn., Stamford Museum and Nature Center, Nov., 1961; New York, A.C.A. Galleries, *Lester Avnet Collection*, Sept. 18-Oct. 18, 1969; Smithsonian Institution Traveling Exhibition Service, *The Armand Hammer Collection*, Little Rock, Arkansas, Arkansas Art Center, Nov. 21, 1970-Jan. 12, 1971; San Francisco, California, California Palace of the Legion of Honor, *The Armand Hammer Collection*, Feb. 11-Mar. 14, 1971; Oklahoma City, Oklahoma, Oklahoma Art Center, *The Armand Hammer Collection*, June 15-July 11, 1971; San Diego, California, Fine Arts Gallery of San Diego, *The Armand Hammer Collection*, July 23-Sept. 5, 1971

Literature: *Catalogue of the 23rd Annual International Exhibition of Paintings*, Carnegie Institute Press, 1924, no. 14

Unlike many of his contemporaries, Prendergast did not embrace the more conservative aspects of Impressionism. Rather, from the beginning he struck out in a direction close to that of the Post-Impressionists and Nabis. Later,

there were even stylistic parallels with the Fauves.

Typical of Prendergast's later painting in oil, this work exhibits nothing of the Realist doctrine generally associated with other members of the Eight group. His subjects were not the crowded streets of the New York slums painted by the Ashcan School, but groups of happy people at their leisure on the beach, in the park, thronging the sunny boulevards of Paris or the bridges of Venice. Figures are generally disposed laterally across the foreground against highly simplified forms of sea and land. The ultimate result is a bright lyrical tapestry of color with shapes loosely defined by a heavy line breaking or fading against shifting planes of color as it approximates contour.

59 Andrew Wyeth (1917-   )
Brandywine Valley, 1940
Watercolor: 21" x 29" (53.3 x 73.7 cm.)
Signed and dated lower right: Andrew Wyeth 1940
Painted at the John Chad house in Chaddsford, Pennsylvania

Exhibitions: Washington, D. C., Smithsonian Institution, *The Armand Hammer Collection*, Mar. 20-May 17, 1970, no. 115 (repr. in cat. supplement); Smithsonian Institution Traveling Exhibition Service, *The Armand Hammer Collection*, Kansas City, Missouri, William Rockhill Nelson Gallery of Art, June 30-Aug. 2, 1970, New Orleans, Louisiana, Isaac Delgado Museum of Art, Aug. 15-Sept. 20, 1970, Columbus, Ohio, Columbus Gallery of Fine Arts, Oct. 9-Nov. 1, 1970, Little Rock, Arkansas, Arkansas Art Center, Nov. 21, 1970-Jan. 12, 1971; San Francisco, California, California Palace of the Legion of Honor, *The Armand Hammer Collection*, Feb. 11-Mar. 14, 1971; Oklahoma City, Oklahoma, Oklahoma Art Center, *The Armand Hammer Collection*, June 15-July 11, 1971

Literature: Sale catalog, *Impressionist, American and Modern Paintings and Watercolors*, Houston, Texas: Christie, Manson & Woods (New York), Apr. 6, 1970, no. 21, p. 19

In contrast to the structure and design of Wyeth's more recent works in drybrush, which have much in common with his tempera paintings, the freely flowing washes of this early example take every advantage of the inherent qualities of transparent watercolor.

The lessons found in the work of such artists as Winslow Homer and the rigorous tutelage of his father helped Wyeth to develop absolute mastery of the medium at an early age. This watercolor, painted more than thirty years ago, reveals his deep involvement with the Brandywine Valley where he still lives and works without regard for contemporary trends in the United States or abroad.

Albrecht Dürer (1471-1528)
Tuft of Cowslips
Gouache on vellum
7⁹/₁₆″ x 6⅝″ (19.2 x 16.8 cm.)
Signed (in later hand): AD; Dated (in another hand): 1526

Collections: Private collection, England; Hal O'Nians,
London

Literature: Jaro Springer, "Dürers Zeichnungen in neuen
Publikationen," *Repertorium für Kunstwissenschaft*, 29,
1906, p. 555f.; Joseph Meder, "Die grüne Passion und die
Tier— und Pflanzenstudien Albrecht Dürers in der
Albertina," *Repertorium für Kunstwissenschaft*, 30, 1907,
p. 181; Sebastian Killermann," A. Dürers Pflanzen und
Tierzeichnungen," *Studien zur deutschen Kunstgeschichte*
119, Strassburg, 1910, pp. 94ff.; Friedrich Winkler,
Die Zeichnungen Albrecht Dürers, Berlin, 1936, II, p. 65ff.;
Heinrich Schwarz, "A Water-colour attributed to Dürer,"
The Burlington Magazine 95, 1953, p. 149ff.;
Hans Kauffmann, "Dürer in der Kunst und im Kunsturteil
um 1600," *Anzeiger des Germanischen Nationalmuseums
in Nürnberg*, 1940-1953, 1954, p. 29; Otto Benesch,
Master Drawings in the Albertina, New York: 1967, p. 337;
Charles W. Talbot, ed., *Dürer in America—His Graphic
Work*, Washington, D.C..: The National Gallery of Art,
1971, p. 110, note 3

Until recently, when the *Tuft of Cowslips* was purchased
for the Hammer Collection, the only plant study in this
country credited to Albrecht Dürer was the *Buttercup*
given by Mrs. Charles Bradley to the Museum of Art at
the Rhode Island School of Design. The Rhode Island
drawing forms an integral part of a group of three more
sheets, the *Columbine*, the *Celandine* and the
Three Medicinal Herbs, all at the Albertina in Vienna,
from which, in fact, the *Buttercup* had been separated during
the Napoleonic wars. Similar in technique and style, all
four have in common that they are painted on vellum,
mostly with smooth and opaque gouache; that they depict
wild-growing plants; that a patch of soil is represented
together with the plants; and that a later, collector's hand,
not Dürer's, has added the date 1526 in each case.
In addition, the *Small Piece of Turf*—also in the Albertina—
although undated, is extremely close in style. The date 1526
can also be found on a drawing in Berlin of two cut peonies.
Although this drawing is also painted on vellum, it is
somewhat different in style.

Most of these flower pieces can be clearly identified with
drawings acquired after 1588 by Emperor Rudolf II
in Prague from Anna Imhoff in Nuremberg. The Imhoffs
had bought many of them in 1560 from the widow of
Endres Dürer, Albrecht's brother, but the Imhoff family
also bought from other sources (e.g. from the heirs of
Paul Koler), so that this provenance does not guarantee

absolute authenticity. In fact, Dürer's authorship of all of
these drawings has been doubted by scholars, but no
satisfactory alternative has yet been found. The work of the
Dürer imitator Hans Hoffmann, active in Nuremberg in the
second half of the sixteenth century (in time to slip his
works into the Imhoff Collection before its sale to the
Emperor), seems to be quite different, as Hans Kauffmann
has explained so well. Like Joseph Meder and Otto Benesch,
the directors of the Albertina, Hans Kauffmann can be
counted among the defenders of Dürer's authorship
for the group.

The immediacy of observation from life is expressed in
these plant studies by the patches of soil and by the
representation of accidental weeds and grasses together
with the flowers. This trait they share only with some of
the plants in the paintings of great Netherlandish artists
like Hugo van der Goes or with the only surely accepted
plant study by Dürer, the *Great Piece of Turf*, also in the
Albertina in Vienna and dated 1503 by Dürer himself.

The *Great Piece of Turf*, painted on paper mainly in
watercolor with only some touches of gouache, not only
has a greater transparency of color but also more emphasis
on line in shading and contour. For these reasons it is
comparable to several studies, all painted on paper,
of single, cut garden flowers in Bremen and elsewhere.
If one accepts Dürer's authorship for both groups, technique
may be one of the reasons for the differences between them.
But the differences might also be explained by different
dates of execution.

There is another, still somewhat different drawing in the
Albertina, the small *Nosegay of Violets*. Painted on vellum
and very likely identical to one in the Imhoff list, it is done
in a somewhat coarser, freer gouache, at least in the
treatment of the leaves.

The newcomer to these plant studies, the *Tuft of Cowslips*,
is interesting in many ways. It is painted on vellum with
some watercolor and more gouache, and, as do most of
the vellum group, it bears the date 1526. At one time,
therefore, it must have belonged to the same collection.
The dark color of the patch of soil is also closely related
to the rest of the group. The color of the leaves, however,
totally lacks the smoothness of the leaves of the vellum
group and is much more lively and more transparently
applied. In fact, when closely compared, the highly
differentiated greens of the *Tuft of Cowslips* seem to
correspond almost exactly to those in the *Great
Piece of Turf*. In particular, the strong light green
of the highlights on the leaves of the foreground is
absolutely identical to the most strident green in the work
in the Albertina. On the other hand, the loose application
of just these touches is most closely related to the
execution of the leaves of the bunch of violets in the
same collection. Although the *Tuft of Cowslips* has none of
the linear quality typical of the paper group, it corresponds

to the *Great Piece of Turf* in the spatial depth, in the richness of the observation of light, and in the life emanating from the plant. The tender trefoil of clover appearing in the center amidst the thicker leaves of the cowslip illustrates both the delicacy of the artist's technique and his refinement of observation. The velvety, rich surfaces of some of the leaves farther back is equally strong testimony for the drawing having been created by an artist of the highest standards.

The Hammer drawing thus offers a new perspective on the whole group of flower pieces. An artist like Dürer, whose means vary with the object and with his objectives, and whose watercolors of landscape include the miniature-like density of his view of Innsbruck, the impressionistic looseness of his view of the valley near Kalkreuth, and the graphic clarity of the wooden covered bridge called *Trockensteg* in his native Nuremberg, can well be credited with different methods of executing plants. The *Tuft of Cowslips* may well be the centerpiece which ties the three different groups together. In spatial richness and liveliness and in delicacy of color, it is far closer than any other of the vellum group to the *Great Piece of Turf*.

The Hammer drawing was, in fact, taken to the Albertina and there put side by side with the *Great Piece of Turf*. After intense study the curators of the Albertina, including Dr. Walter Koschatzky, Dr. Alice Strobl, and Dr. Konrad Oberhuber, were all convinced that the Hammer drawing was undoubtedly by the same hand that created the *Great Piece of Turf*.

61 Raphael Sanzio (1483-1520)
Study for a Fresco with Hosea and Jonah
Pen and brown wash, heightened with white over preparation in black chalk and stylus, squared with stylus and red chalk
10⅝" x 7¹³/₁₆" (26.2 x 19.8 cm.)

Collections: J. Richardson, Sr.; J. Richardson, Jr., London (Frits Lugt, *Marque des Collections*, no. 2170); P. J. Mariette, Paris (Lugt 2097); H. C. Jennings, London (Lugt 2771); P. Payne Knight; Baron H. de Triquety, Paris (Lugt 1304); E. Colando, Paris (Lugt 837); Major S. V. Christie-Miller C.B.E.

Literature: Jonathan Richardson, *An Account of the Statues, Bas-Reliefs, Drawings and Pictures in Italy, France, etc., with remarks by Mr. Richardson, Sen. and Jun.* (2nd ed.), London, 1754, p. 104; C. Metz, *Imitations of Ancient and Modern Drawings*, London, 1798, pl. XXXXIV; J. D. Passavant, *Raphael d'Urbin*, Paris, 1860, vol. II, p. 142; F. A. Gruyer, *Raphaël et l'Antiquité*, Paris, 1846, vol. I, p. 379, n. 1; C. Ruland, *The Works of Raphael Santi da Urbino As Represented in the Raphael Collection in the Royal Library at Windsor Castle*, London, 1876, p. 271, vol. III, 4; J. A. Crowe and G. B. Cavalcaselle, *Raphael,*

Life and Works, London, 1882-85, vol. II, p. 216, note; G. E. Lafenestre and E. Richtenberger, *Rome, Le Vatican et les Eglises*, Paris, 1903, p. 263; Oskar Fischel, "Some Lost Drawings By or Near Raphael," *The Burlington Magazine*, 20, 1912, p. 299, pl. II, fig. 12; Oskar Fischel, under "Santi," in Thieme-Becker, *Allgemeines Lexikon der Bildenden Künstler*, 29, 1935, p. 438; Oscar Fischel, *Raphael*, London, 1948, vol. I, p. 364; L. Dussler, *Raphael, A Critical Catalogue of his Pictures, Wall-Paintings and Tapestries*, London, 1971, p. 94

In the winter of 1510-1511 Pope Julius II was absent from Rome for a considerable time. We know that during this period Michelangelo did not progress with his work on the Sistine ceiling for lack of funds, and it is highly probable that Raphael encountered similar difficulties. Very likely it was at that time that Agostino Chigi, the rich Sienese banker and one of the greatest patrons of Renaissance Rome, commissioned Raphael to design and partly execute the decoration of his chapel in the church of Santa Maria della Pace in Rome. All that was painted were the prophets high on the walls flanking the window in the lunette about the cornice and the sibyls on the face of the arch below the cornice and above the altar niche. Because these were the most accessible frescoes by the great master, they were among his most admired creations. Over the centuries, unfortunately, the condition of the frescoes has deteriorated. The prophets are overpainted; the sibyls, although restored, have lost some of their original freshness. As a result, their fame has been eclipsed by the Stanze, well-presented and now readily accessible as part of the Vatican Museums.

Since the prophets high above the cornice are difficult to decipher from below, the Hammer drawing is of special value in giving us an idea of this great work. It represents the group at the left of the window, Jonah and Hosea, both predicting, as all the other seers do, the Resurrection of Christ and of the dead. The drawing is finished to a large degree. As indicated by the drawings preserved for the pendant, the figures of the prophets must have been prepared in many small sketches and in detailed studies after the model. In fact, Raphael squared the paper with a stylus to facilitate his drawing the figures of the prophets in exact scale. He drew first in black chalk and then with pen. While the ink was still partially wet on the right side, he washed in the shadows with large and rapid touches of the brush and then added the white highlights which give such great life to Jonah's face. These grand, finished figures recall both the philosophers of the School of Athens that Raphael had painted only a short time before and Michelangelo's ideas for the tomb of Julius II, with which Raphael must have been familiar.

Quite different from the prophets is the figure of the angel, rapidly sketched in with a freer pen over some preparation with the stylus. Only the most important shading is added. We know from early sketches that this angel was originally placed in a slightly different, much more hidden position, behind Jonah. He is now given greater prominence. As is customary with Raphael, the figure is drawn in the nude to give a better idea of the movement. The angel differs, therefore, from the work as executed where he wears a cloak around his thigh. Raphael had second thoughts about the angel's left arm. It was at first lightly indicated somewhat higher than it appears in the final version. When the drawing was finished, Raphael covered it with another net of lines in red chalk to transfer it, probably directly, to the cartoon. But for some minor changes and the exceptions noted here, the fresco corresponds very closely to the drawing.

None of the authors who have written about the drawing in recent times have had the opportunity to see it, and most of the older authors knew it only from the facsimile done by Metz. Fischel, publishing the old photo in Windsor Castle, was at first hesitant to pass judgment but later seems to have thought that the drawing was by Giulio Romano. This idea was possible only because he dated the fresco 1514, when Giulio was already active. Dussler, judging exclusively from Fischel's reproduction, gave it more generally to the School of Raphael, knowing well that in 1511 Giulio was too young to have done such a work. However, no serious activity is recorded for any of the other members of Raphael's school at that time, and the insight into the creative process that the drawing affords precludes any possibility of regarding it as a copy. In fact, as James Byam Shaw has commented, when the drawing is seen in the original, its quality makes it abundantly clear that only Raphael can have been the author. It corresponds well to other of Raphael's drawings for the Stanza della Segnatura. In fact, in its combination of highly finished parts and loosely drawn sections, it must be considered among the most representative of Raphael's drawings of that period. It will be included in volume 10 of *Raphaels Zeichnungen*, begun in 1913 by Oskar Fischel and continued at present by Konrad Oberhuber.

62 Antonio Allegri da Correggio (1494-1534)
Recto: *Pendentive Study with Sts. Matthew and Jerome*
Ink and red chalk: 8¼″ x 5½″ (21.0 x 14.0 cm.)
Verso: *Study for the "Madonna della Scodella"*
Ink and red chalk: 7¹⁵/₁₆″ x 5″ (20.2 x 12.7 cm.)

Collections: Sir Peter Lely, London; P. and D. Colnaghi & Co., Ltd., London; Michael Hirst, London

Exhibitions: Edinburgh, The Arts Council of Scotland, *Exhibition of Italian 16th Century Drawings from British Private Collections*, Aug. 1969; San Francisco, California, California Palace of the Legion of Honor, *The Armand Hammer Collection*, Feb. 11-Mar. 14, 1971; Oklahoma City, Oklahoma, Oklahoma Art Center, *The Armand Hammer Collection*, June 15-July 11, 1971

Literature: Konrad Oberhuber, "Drawings by Artists Working in Parma in the Sixteenth Century," *Master Drawings*, vol. VIII, no. 3, 1970, pp. 278-279, pl. 30 (recto), pl. 31 (verso)

This double sheet has been fully published by Konrad Oberhuber in a review of A. E. Popham's *Italian Drawings in the Department of Prints and Drawings in the British Museum, Artists Working in Parma in the Sixteenth Century*, 1967, which appeared in *Master Drawings*, vol. VIII, no. 3, 1970, pp. 278-279.

According to Dr. Oberhuber's analysis, these studies are the earliest by the artist so far known for the two works listed above. This accounts for the changes, as well as the divergences from the final versions and the rudeness of the draftsmanship.

Several other preliminary drawings exist for the pendentive fresco, but the verso of the Hammer sheet is apparently one of only two known sketches for the altarpiece, the *Rest on the Flight into Egypt*, also called the *Madonna della Scodella* ("Madonna with the plate"), dated 1530, which is now in the Gallery of Parma. The other sketch, which is in the Uffizi, was considered a copy by Corrado Ricci but was accepted as genuine by A. E. Popham (*Correggio's Drawings*, 1957, cat. no. 76).

Although the majority of Correggio's drawings were executed in natural red chalk, he sometimes enforced this medium with pen and ink (to increase the definition of the form) beyond that of his initial sketch. Correggio was not a beautiful or polished draftsman in the same sense, for example, as were Leonardo or Raphael. He was largely self-taught in the art of drawing, and he used the medium chiefly to work out facets of his paintings and frescoes. Lineal grace and rhythm were not his concerns as his approach was painterly rather than graphic. The various stages of his drawings as he developed and altered his ideas for compositions are reflected in their varying techniques. Some are broad in execution and well-defined, others composed of numerous alterations and re-drawing in the search for their final form. The present double sheet is an example of the latter type. It is perhaps less characteristic of the artist than his better known, pure chalk drawings, but in its technique and re-work it agrees with several of his other designs. The contouring of the figures of the *Madonna della Scodella* study, for example, is similar to that found on the recto of the Louvre drawing of several *putti* (Popham 28). The Louvre drawing relates to the artist's fresco in the apse of S. Giovanni Evangelista.

63 Rembrandt van Rijn (1606-1669)
A Biblical Subject
Pen and ink, brown wash, heightened with white

6 13/16" x 6¾" (17.3 x 17.2 cm.)
Watermark: Arms of Amsterdam

Collection: B. F. Nicholson (Sale, London, Sotheby & Co.,
Mar. 23, 1971, no. 90)

Exhibition: Oklahoma City, Oklahoma, Oklahoma Art
Center, *The Armand Hammer Collection*, June 15-Sept. 5,
1971

An elderly king, wearing a turban surmounted by a crown,
and holding a sceptre in his right hand, is seated on a
throne beneath a baldschin. On the right, two female figures
kneel side by side before him. The woman on the left clasps
something on her knee.

The king is similar in type to the artist's representation
of Biblical kings, such as David in the drawing of
Nathan Admonishing David, ca. 1655, in the Metropolitan
Museum (Benesch 948). He also bears a strong affinity to a
number of the figures in the copies Rembrandt made after
Moghul miniatures in the mid-'50s (Benesch 1187-1206),
suggesting that the artist drew inspiration from these for
his representation of an Old Testament figure.

The subject is not easily elucidated. The suggested
identification of the Judgment of Solomon, made in the
sale catalog, is not entirely convincing. In the first place
it is by no means certain that the woman on the left holds a
baby. The object could equally well be a jar. Secondly, the
position of the second woman suggests that she is an
attendant and not a rival. The scene depicted here must
represent a woman humbly making some offering to an
elderly king.

This sheet, which until its recent appearance in the
sale-room was unknown, is comparable to a number of
late Rembrandt drawings, in particular *Isaac and Rebecca
Spied Upon by Abimelach*, in a private collection,
New York (Benesch 988), which has been variously dated
in the late '50s or early '60s (for a discussion of this
drawing which favors the latter dating, see *Rembrandt
Drawings from American Collections*, Pierpont Morgan
Library, Fogg Art Museum, 1960, no. 76). The delineation
of the couple in this study is notably similar to that of the
two kneeling women in the present sheet.

64 Jean Antoine Watteau (1684-1721)
Young Girl
Red and black chalk: 8½" x 5¾" (21.6 x 14.6 cm.)

Collections: Philippe Wiener, Paris; Albert Meyer (Sale,
Paris, May 24-June 8, 1935, no. 100); Mrs. Jesse I. Straus,
New York

Exhibitions: London, Royal Academy of Arts, *The London
Exhibition of French Art, 1200-1900*, Jan.-Mar. 1932,
no. 713, cat. no. 765 (lent by Albert Meyer); Paris, Jean A.
Seligmann, *Collection Albert Meyer*, May 24-June 8, 1935,

no. 100; Smithsonian Institution Traveling Exhibition
Service, *The Armand Hammer Collection*, Little Rock,
Arkansas, Arkansas Art Center, Nov. 21, 1970-Jan. 12,
1971; San Francisco, California, California Palace of the
Legion of Honor, *The Armand Hammer Collection*, Feb.
11-Mar. 14, 1971; Oklahoma City, Oklahoma, Oklahoma
Art Center, *The Armand Hammer Collection*, June 15-July
11, 1971; San Diego, California, Fine Arts Gallery of San
Diego, *The Armand Hammer Collection*, July 23-Sept.
5, 1971

Literature: Edmond de Goncourt, *Catalogue Raisonné de
l'Oeuvre Peint, Dessiné et Gravé d'Antoine Watteau*, Paris:
Rapilly, 1875, no. 652, p. 297; Seymour de Ricci, *Catalogue
de Dessins de Maîtres du XVIIIème Siècle, Collection Albert
Meyer*, Paris: Jean A. Seligmann, 1935, no. 100, repr. opp.;
*Commemorative Catalogue of the London Exhibition of
French Art, 1200-1900*, London: Royal Academy of Arts,
1933, no. 765, p. 163; K. T. Parker and J. Mathey, *Catalogue
de l'Oeuvre Dessiné d'Antoine Watteau*, Paris: F. de Nobele,
1957, vol. II, no. 577, p. 312, repr. pl. 577; *The Irma N.
Straus Collection of Old Master Drawings*, New York:
Parke-Bernet Galleries, Inc., Oct. 21, 1970, no. 21, repr. in
color p. 37

Watteau had a predilection for a feminine type which
appears in nearly all of his drawings of girls and women.
The face was a full oval, the nose slightly *retroussé* with
large nostrils, the eyes heavy-lidded, long-lashed, oval
shaped, almost slanted, the lips full, the chin plump, and
the hair generally drawn up tightly into a knot on the top
of the head. In the Hammer portrait—a study which has not
been related to a painting—this easily recognized type
appears. The modesty and restraint of the model's pose
imply that she was drawn from life, a strong likelihood
since it is well known that Watteau made hundreds of figure
studies which he kept in bound volumes and drew upon as
elements for his pictures.

This elegantly dressed young lady looks down, but
whether in reverie or shyness it is difficult to determine.
Watteau has drawn her face in red chalk, touching her
eyebrows lightly with black. The red chalk has taken on
the grain of the paper, giving it a porous quality. The hair
is only briefly indicated by delicate lines, the paper itself
left to convey it. Certain of the deep red accents, such as
those on the bow of the necklace and on the lips, suggest
that the chalk was moistened. Heavy black shading sets the
figure off at the right. Despite her youth, the girl, whom
the artist has represented with great sympathy, has an
expression of maturity.

Watteau's great friend, Comte de Caylus, has been
credited by Seymour de Ricci with having engraved the
girl's head in his *Figures de différentes caractères*, no. 273.
On the other hand, Parker-Mathey and E. Dacier attribute
the engraving to Laurent Cars.

65 Jean Antoine Watteau (1684-1721)
Couple Seated on a Bank
Red, black, and white chalk on buff paper
9½" x 13¾" (24.1 x 34.9 cm.)
Signed lower right in ink: Vataux fecit
Written in crayon lower left: Watteau

Collections: Anonymous Sale (Paris, 1892, no. 72);
Lallemand (Sale, Paris, May 2, 1894); Léon Michel-Lévy
(Sale, Paris, Galerie Georges Petit, June 17-18, 1925, no.
106); George Blumenthal, New York; Mrs. Jesse I. Straus,
New York

Exhibitions: Paris, Galerie Georges Petit, *Collection Léon
Michel-Lévy*, June 17-18, 1925, no. 106; London, Royal
Academy of Arts, *The London Exhibition of French Art,
1200-1900*, Jan. 4-Mar. 12, 1932, no. 738, cat. no. 780 (lent
by George Blumenthal); Buffalo, Buffalo Fine Arts Gallery,
*Master Drawings . . . from . . . Museums and Private
Collections of America*, no. 60, pl. 60; Smithsonian
Institution Traveling Exhibition Service, *The Armand
Hammer Collection*, Little Rock, Arkansas, Arkansas Art
Center, Nov. 21, 1970-Jan. 12, 1971; San Francisco,
California, California Palace of the Legion of Honor, *The
Armand Hammer Collection*, Feb. 11-Mar. 14, 1971;
Oklahoma City, Oklahoma, Oklahoma Art Center, *The
Armand Hammer Collection*, June 15-July 11, 1971; San
Diego, California, Fine Arts Gallery of San Diego, *The
Armand Hammer Collection*, July 23-Sept. 5, 1971

Literature: *Les Maîtres du Dessin*, Paris, 1911, vol. III, pl.
136; K. T. Parker, *The Drawings of Antoine Watteau*,
London: B. T. Batsford, Ltd., 1931, pl. 92; *Commemorative
Catalog of the London Exhibition of French Art, 1200-1900*,
London: Royal Academy of Arts, 1933, no. 780, p. 165; K. T.
Parker and J. Mathey, *Catalogue de l'Oeuvre Dessiné
d'Antoine Watteau*, Paris: F. de Nobele, 1957, no. 665,
p. 326, repr. pl. 665; *The Irma N. Straus Collection of Master
Drawings*, New York: Parke-Bernet Galleries, Inc., Oct. 21,
1970, no. 20, p. 34

The great beauty of Watteau's best drawings stems
primarily from two factors, the sensitive precision of his
line and the enchanting coloristic effects created by his use
of three crayons, black, red, and white. These features are
brilliantly embodied in this sheet. Although the preliminary
figures are not shown in the positions they hold in the
paintings for which they served, the artist has drawn them
in a remarkable way. The arms of the young man serve as
an arc to support the figure of the girl; the index finger of
his left hand points directly to the nape of her neck; and
the right hands of both figures rest parallel to each other on
the ground. The juxtaposition of unrelated, yet
harmoniously arranged figures gives this drawing a fresh,
spontaneous character. In contrast to the extreme
foreshortening of the man and the sketchiness of his

delineation is the complete, detailed rendering of the girl,
which adds to the visual impact of the work.

Although Watteau was never in Italy, he is known to have
studied the work of Paolo Veronese in Paris. A measure of
the elegance, and indeed the fineness of the features of his
faces, is undoubtedly derived from the great Venetian
master.

The graceful gentleman in the Hammer study appears in at
least two Watteau paintings: *La Famille*, in the Rothschild
Collection, engraved by Aveline (Dacier-Vuaflart, *Jean de
Jullienne et les graveurs de Watteau . . .* , III, 1922, no 86);
and *Assemblée Galante* (Dacier-Vuaflart 139).

The sitters in *La Famille* have been identified, on the basis
of a document of 1777, as members of the family of Jean
Le Bouc-Santussan, a master goldsmith who married the
daughter of the famed art dealer, E. P. Gersaint, with whom
Watteau lodged for a while.

The *Assemblée Galante* belonged to a French countess who
was the mistress of the Duke of Savoy for several years
before she returned to Paris where she became the leader of
a salon frequented by many great *amateurs* of Watteau.
The *Assemblée Galante* was one of two major Watteaus in
her sale of 1737, which took place a year after her death.

66 Giovanni Battista Tiepolo (1696-1770)
Virgin and Child Adored by Bishops, Monks, and Women
Pen and bister wash over the black chalk on white paper
16¾" x 11¹³/₁₆" (42.5 x 30.0 cm.)

Collections: Prince Alexis Orloff (Sale, Paris, Galerie
Georges Petit, Apr. 29-30, 1920, no. 134); W. W. Crocker,
Burlingame, California; Augustus Pollack, Monterey,
California; R. M. Light & Co., Inc., Boston

Exhibitions: San Francisco, San Francisco Museum of Art,
The Opening Exhibition, Jan.-Mar. 1935; Chicago, Art
Institute of Chicago, *Loan Exhibition of Paintings, Drawings
and Prints by the Two Tiepolos: Giambattista and
Giandomenico*, Feb. 4-Mar. 6, 1938, no. 47; Cambridge,
Massachusetts, Harvard University, Fogg Museum of Art,
Seventy Master Drawings, Nov. 27, 1948-Jan. 6, 1949, no. 46

Literature: Otto Benesch, *Venetian Drawings of the 18th
Century in America*, New York: H. Bittner & Co., 1947, no.
19, p. 31, pl. 19; Agnes Mongan, *One Hundred Masters
Drawings*, Cambridge: Harvard University Press, 1949, p.
106, repr. opp.; George Knox, "The Orloff Album of Tiepolo
Drawings," *The Burlington Magazine*, London, June 1961,
vol. CIII, no. 15, p. 275

The subject of this drawing is not yet fully identified
although the Virgin is obviously showing favor,
recommending, or interceding for the kneeling male figure
at the left. The loose long hair and seemingly unclerical
attire of this figure do not readily suggest a relationship to a

religious order or with a familiar saint. The object which he holds in his left hand may be a small book.

The drawing comes from the well-known *Orloff Album* which was sold in Paris in 1920. According to Knox, the album had been assembled by a Russian dilettante, Gregory Vladimirovtich Orloff (1777-1826), who published a book on Italian painting. Later the collection was inherited by Prince Alexis Orloff. The ninety-six leaves from the album included several which were highly finished and were often referred to as presentation drawings.

Benesch and Agnes Mongan have ascribed the drawing to Tiepolo's mature period since it is looser in treatment than the preceding work *(Saint Jerome in the Desert)*, but the dark wash which serves to accentuate the forms is still distributed in the same highly pictorial manner as in the earlier work. The contouring by means of a firm continuous line, characteristic of the earlier style, gives way here to the broken, accented strokes and modeling by flat washes which herald the increasingly fugitive means which the artist adopted in his later drawings.

In the Hammer work the figure of Saint John can be compared generally to the larger figure of Saint Sebastian in the Fogg Art Museum's drawing entitled *The Holy Family Enthroned with Saints Sebastian, Catherine of Alexandria and Francis*, dated by Knox about 1735. Based on this comparison, the Hammer drawing can probably be assigned the same date rather than Benesch's suggested date of about 1740.

67 Giovanni Battista Tiepolo (1696-1770)
St. Jerome in the Desert Listening to the Angels
Pen and brown ink, brown wash, heightened with white, over black chalk on buff paper
16¾″ x 10⅞″ (42.5 x 27.6 cm.)

Collections: Formerly in the collection of the Venetian engraver, Pietro Monaco (1707-1772), engraved and published by him in 1743 in his *Raccolta di Centododici Stampe di Pitture della Storia Sacra*, and then re-issued with additional plates in 1763; Ann Payne Robertson (on loan to The Metropolitan Museum of Art)

Exhibitions: San Francisco, California, California Palace of the Legion of Honor, *The Armand Hammer Collection*, Feb. 11-Mar. 14, 1971; Oklahoma City, Oklahoma, Oklahoma Art Center, *The Armand Hammer Collection*, June 15-July 11, 1971

Literature: Sale catalog, *Important Old Master Drawings*, London: Sotheby & Co., Nov. 26, 1970, no. 71, p. 113, repr. opp.

This splendid work by Tiepolo belongs to a group of very finished drawings which the artist probably intended for sale. Other drawings of a similar type are in the Museo Civico, Bassano; Museo Civico di Storia ed Arte, Trieste; the

Art Institute of Chicago; the Cleveland Museum of Art; the Kunstinstitut, Frankfort; and the Royal Museum of Fine Arts, Copenhagen.*

These drawings have been placed chronologically in the 1730s and were surely executed by the end of the decade since they were engraved by Pietro Monaco in 1740. Drawn in pen and rich brown washes, the drawings are heightened with white, a feature which Max Goering attributes to the influence upon Tiepolo by the French artist Louis Dorigny (1654-1742), who worked for many years in Venice and died in Verona.

Tiepolo, who must be considered one of history's most brilliant draftsmen, began his career as a *tenebroso* who worked with strong effects of light and shadow to create relief and depth. The present drawing reflects this chiaroscuro treatment as well as the artist's use of continuous binding lines to define the forms, both distinctive of his early style. The free application of the wash and the heavy dark accents create a fluid, dramatic background pattern for a drawing which has the monumental quality of an altarpiece. This solidity of execution, still founded in the Emilian influence upon Tiepolo's earlier work, affords the utmost contrast to the dissolving weightlessness and radiant light of his later drawings.

George Knox has proposed the name of Giovanni Raggi (1712-1792), a disciple of Tiepolo, as the author of a copy of this drawing which is in the Museo Correr, Venice.

*A copy is in the Civico Museo Correr, Venice (inv. 4596, pl. 29) and was published by George Knox, "A Group of Tiepolo Drawings Owned and Engraved by Pietro Monaco," in *Master Drawings*, vol. III, Apr. 1966, no. 4, p. 389, pl. 18. Another copy was in the collection of Francis Watson in London; see also Linda Boyer, letter, *Master Drawings*, vol. IV, no. 2, 1966.

68 François Boucher (1703-1770)
Venus Reclining against a Dolphin
Black chalk heightened with white
9″ x 13½″ (22.8 x 34.3 cm.)

Collections: Charles E. Slatkin Galleries, Inc., New York; Norton Simon, Los Angeles

Exhibitions: Oklahoma City, Oklahoma, Oklahoma Art Center, *The Armand Hammer Collection*, June 15-July 11, 1971; San Diego, California, Fine Arts Gallery of San Diego, *The Armand Hammer Collection*, July 23-Sept. 5, 1971

Literature: Marcel Roux, *Inventaire du Fonds Français, Graveurs du XVIIIeme Siècle*, Paris: Bibliothèque Nationale, Départment des Estampes, 1949, vol. IV, no. 88, p. 367; Alexandre Ananoff, *L'Oeuvre Dessiné de François Boucher*, Catalogue Raisonné, Paris: F. de Nobele, vol. I, no. 801A, p. 208 (counterproof), (engraved by Demarteau); Sale catalog, *Property of the Norton Simon Foundation and Old Master Drawings and Paintings, from the Private Collection of Norton Simon,* New York: Parke-Bernet Galleries, Inc., May 7, 1971, no. 206, p. 158, repr. opp.

Among the artists of the Rococo, Boucher was the leading reviver of mythological subjects and the interpreter of the female nude who endowed it with the greatest degree of voluptuousness. The obvious sensuousness of his nudes contrasts, for example, with the non-sensual, classically influenced nudes of Rubens.

Boucher executed about fifty drawings on the theme of Venus, "the divinity adored by the courtiers of the age of Louis XV." Several studies by Boucher show the goddess in a reclining position, similar to that of the present work, but with different attributes. The Hammer drawing is a rare Boucher counterproof, reinforced by the artist. The location of its counterpart is not known at present.

In Boucher's time counterproofs were made when the chalk medium was still quite fresh and susceptible to transfer. This was done by means of skillful rubbing after the backs of both the first drawing and of the blank sheet were moistened to assist in the process. The artist could then rework the transferred impression and have the reversed composition as another "original" after his first original drawing. This method was also practiced by Fragonard who was compelled by the great demand for his drawings to use this quasi-print technique. Boucher, on the other hand, had students make replicas of his drawings, and counterproofs are not frequent in his work. In the eighteenth century many collectors preferred counterproofs because they were more "delicate" in tone than the designs from which they were pressed. Unlike prints, however, a counterproof, like a monotype, did not yield more than one acceptable impression.

69 François Boucher (1703-1770)
Landscape with a Rustic Bridge, ca. 1740
Black chalk, heightened with white on buff paper
8" x 10¾" (20.3 x 27.3 cm.)

Collections: Fernand Javel, Paris; Charles E. Slatkin Galleries, Inc., New York; Norton Simon, Los Angeles

Exhibitions: Oklahoma City, Oklahoma, Oklahoma Art Center, *The Armand Hammer Collection,* June 15-July 11, 1971; San Diego, California, Fine Arts Gallery of San Diego, *The Armand Hammer Collection,* July 23-Sept. 5, 1971

Literature: *Great Drawings of All Time, French: 13th Century to 1919* (selected and edited by Ira Moskowitz, text by Agnes Mongan), New York: Shorewood Publishers, Inc., 1962, vol. III, no. 696, repr. opp.; Sale catalog, *Property of the Norton Simon Foundation and Old Master Drawings and Paintings, from the Private Collection of Norton Simon,* New York: Parke-Bernet Galleries, Inc., May 7, 1971, no. 207, p. 160, repr. opp.

Fully published by Agnes Mongan in *Great Drawings of All Time* (Shorewood, 1962, vol. III, no. 696), this drawing is assigned to the period of 1740 when Boucher, then designing for tapestries, made frequent trips into the country en route to Beauvais and the Gobelins.

It is noteworthy that in his own time Boucher was roundly criticized by the Revolutionists for his pastoral paintings; his countryside was considered romantic and his peasants disguised aristocrats. But a truer note came out in his landscape drawings. Here Boucher took his cue from such Dutch masters as Jacob Ruisdael and Jan van Goyen who were among the artists whose work he collected and studied. In consequence, his landscape drawings have a tranquility and restraint which contrast with the energetic sensuousness of his figural works. On the whole, the figures in his landscape drawings are subordinated to the setting, sometimes, as in the present work, appearing as staffage.

Boucher is known to have formed his drawing style upon that of Watteau whom he copied and engraved. It was this influence which led him to develop his supple contouring and expressive accenting of light and dark. However, the thirty years that separated the two artists can be detected in the change from the older artist's straight, uninterrupted line to the undulant, rococo forms of the younger man. But Boucher's landscape drawings were still marked by a firm lineality in which short flecks of the crayon delineated the foliage and lead white was added to create the shimmer of light in the distance.

70 Jean-Honoré Fragonard (1723-1806)
Visit to the Nurse
Chinese ink wash, heightened with watercolor
12" x 15" (30.5 x 38.1 cm.)

Collections: Frédéric Villot (Sale, Paris, Hôtel Drouot, May 16-18, 1859, no. 122); E. H. Molyneux, Neuilly-sur-Seine; H. Walferdin (Sale, Paris, Apr. 12-16, 1880, no. 200); Prince A. d'Arenberg, Paris; Jacques Seligmann, Paris; Mrs. Jesse I. Straus, New York

Exhibitions: Berlin, Académie Royale des Arts, *Exposition d'Oeuvres de l'Art Français au XVIIIᵉᵐᵉ Siècle,* Jan.-Mar. 1910, no. 178; Paris, Musée Carnavalet, *La Vie Parisienne au XVIIIᵉᵐᵉ Siècle,* Mar. 20-Apr. 30, 1928, no. 166; Paris, Galerie Jacques Seligmann et Fils, Ancien Hôtel de Sagan, *Exposition de Dessins de Fragonard, Pour la Maison Santé au Gardien de la Paix,* May 9-30, 1931, no. 22; Smithsonian Institution Traveling Exhibition Service, *The Armand Hammer Collection,* Little Rock, Arkansas, Arkansas Art Center, Nov. 21, 1970-Jan. 12, 1971; San Francisco, California, California Palace of the Legion of Honor, *The Armand Hammer Collection,* Feb. 11-Mar. 14, 1971; Oklahoma City, Oklahoma, Oklahoma Art Center, *The Armand Hammer Collection,* June 15-July 11, 1971

Literature: Sale catalog, *Catalogue de la Vente M. F. Villot, Dessins, Miniatures et Estampes*, Paris: Hôtel Drouot, 1859, no. 122, p. 20; Académie Royale des Arts, *Catalogue de l'Exposition d'Oeuvres de l'Art Français au XVIIIeme Siècle*, Berlin: La Société Photographiques, 1910, no. 178, p. 41; Louis Réau, *Fragonard, Sa Vie et Son Oeuvre*, Brussels: Elsevier, 1956, pp. 81, 206; Sale catalog, *The Irma N. Straus Collection of Old Master Drawings*, New York: Parke-Bernet Galleries, Inc., Oct. 21, 1970, no. 30, p. 54, repr. opp.

Fragonard frequently depicted the same subject in a drawing as well as in a painting. In some instances the drawings were studies for the later painted work; for example, preparatory drawings are known for the *Education of the Virgin*, the oil on panel now in the Hammer Collection.

Portalis (p. 291) lists a painting, the subject of which, like the Hammer drawing of *The Visit to the Nurse*, was taken from *Miss Sara*, an English novel which had been translated into French. *The Visit to the Nurse* portrays the theme of parental affection and pride. The treatment of the subject almost suggests, or parallels, an Adoration of the Child in religious art. All the figures are assembled on the foreground plane, with the light from the upper left trained on the *paterfamilias* who holds his infant. The graded layers of the gray washes throw the illuminated figures into brilliant relief, as though the scene were taking place on a stage.

Presenting a polar contrast to his celebrated works on the theme of love, the familial themes in Fragonard's oeuvre reflected eighteenth-century French society's pleasure in intimate home-life episodes. Such episodes were most popularly portrayed in the work of Fragonard's contemporary, J. B. Greuze. But while the latter, strongly reflecting the ideas of Rousseau and Diderot, frequently infused moralistic and didactic precepts into his art, Fragonard, although partaking of the "sentimentality" of his era, was free of the social propaganda advanced by the revolutionists. As is well known, Fragonard did not fit into the new order after the French Revolution. Rather, he quickly declined in status, eventually dying in poverty and obscurity in his native city of Grasse.

71 Jean-Honoré Fragonard (1732-1806)
The Little Preacher
Brown wash over black chalk
13¾" x 18¼" (34.9 x 46.7 cm.)

Collections: Anonymous Sale (Paris, May 31, 1790, no. 180); M. Marmontel (Sale, Paris, Hôtel Drouot, Jan. 25-26, 1883, no. 100); Richard Lion (Sale, Paris, Hôtel Drouot, Apr. 3, 1886, no. 40); M. P. Ledoux (Sale, Paris, Galerie Georges Petit, Mar. 5, 1918, no. 27); Adrien Fauchier-Magnan, Neuilly-sur-Seine; Arthur Veil-Picard, Paris; Guiraud Brothers, Paris; Mrs. Jesse I. Straus, New York

Exhibitions: Smithsonian Institution Traveling Exhibition Service, *The Armand Hammer Collection*, Little Rock, Arkansas, Arkansas Art Center, Nov. 21, 1970-Jan. 12, 1971; San Francisco, California, California Palace of the Legion of Honor, *The Armand Hammer Collection*, Feb. 11-Mar. 14, 1971; Oklahoma City, Oklahoma, Oklahoma Art Center, *The Armand Hammer Collection*, June 15-July 11, 1971; San Diego, California, Fine Arts Gallery of San Diego, *The Armand Hammer Collection*, July 23-Sept. 5, 1971

Literature: Baron Roger Portalis, *Honoré Fragonard, Sa Vie et Son Oeuvre*, Paris: J. Rothschild, 1889, pp. 200, 310; Edmond and Jules de Goncourt, *L'Art du XVIIIeme Siècle—Fragonard*, Paris: Edition 1914, pp. 300-301; *Catalogue des Tableaux Anciens et Modernes, Aquarelles et Dessins de la Vente M. P. Ledoux*, Paris: Galerie Georges Petit, 1918, no. 27, p. 20; *Connaissance des Arts*, Aug. 1956, repr., p. 42; Louis Réau, *Fragonard, Sa Vie et Son Oeuvre*, Brussels: Elsevier, 1956, p. 205, fig. 79, p. 82; Alexandre Ananoff, *L'Oeuvre Dessiné de J.-H. Fragonard, Catalogue Raisonné*, Paris: F. de Nobele, 1961, vol. I, no. 40, p. 45, fig. 18; Sale catalog, *The Irma N. Straus Collection of Old Master Drawings*, New York: Parke-Bernet Galleries, Inc., Oct. 21, 1970, no. 31, p. 56, repr. opp.

Ananoff describes "The Little Preacher" as Fanfan, the son of Fragonard. Engraved with variations by N. de Launay in 1781 as a pendant to *L'Education Fait Tout*, now in the collection of Baron E. de Rothschild (Ananoff, no. 11, fig. 6). This engraving may have been made from the painting of the same subject formerly in the Veil-Picard Collection (Wildenstein, no. 471).

72 Jean-Honoré Fragonard (1732-1816)
Grandfather's Reprimand
Gray-brown wash over black chalk
13½" x 17¾" (34.3 x 45.1 cm.)

Collections: Louis-Antoine-August Rohan-Chabot (Sale, Paris, Dec. 8, 1807, no. 43); Baron Vivant-Denon (Sale, Paris, May 1-19, 1826, no. 732); Baron Brunet-Denon (Sale, Paris, Feb. 2, 1846, no. 269); H. Walferdin (Sale, Paris, Apr. 12-16, 1880, no. 199); Comte de Jaucourt, Paris; Sigismond Bardas, Paris; Georges and Florence Blumenthal (Sale, Paris, Dec. 1-2, 1932, no. 30); Jacques Seligmann, Paris; Mrs. Jesse I. Straus, New York (Sale, New York, Parke-Bernet Galleries, Inc., Oct. 21, 1970, no. 34)

Exhibitions: Paris, Musée des Arts Decoratifs, Pavillon de Marsan, Palais du Louvre, *Exposition d'Oeuvres de J.-H. Fragonard*, June 7-July 10, 1921, no. 133; Smithsonian Institution Traveling Exhibition Service, *The Armand Hammer Collection*, Little Rock, Arkansas, Arkansas Art Center, Nov. 21, 1970-Jan. 12, 1971; San Francisco, California, California Palace of the Legion of Honor,

The Armand Hammer Collection, Feb. 11-Mar. 14, 1971;
Oklahoma City, Oklahoma, Oklahoma Art Center,
The Armand Hammer Collection, June 15-July 11, 1971;
San Diego, California, Fine Arts Gallery of San Diego,
The Armand Hammer Collection, July 23-Sept. 5, 1971

Literature: *Catalogue of the Sale of Baron Vivant-Denon*,
Paris: Imprimerie d'Hippolyte Tilliard, 1826, no. 732, p.
178; Baron Roger Portalis, *Honoré Fragonard, Sa Vie et Son
Oeuvre*, Paris: J. Rothschild, 1889, p. 311; Georges
Wildenstein, *Catalogue de l'Exposition d'Oeuvres de J.-H.
Fragonard*, Musée des Arts Decoratifs, Paris: Frazier-Soye,
1921, no. 133; *Catalogue of the Sale of the Georges and
Florence Blumenthal Collection*, Paris: Galerie Georges
Petit, 1932, no. 30, p. 28, repr. pl. 10; Louis Réau, *Fragonard,
Sa Vie et Son Oeuvre*, Brussels: Elsevier, 1956, p. 206;
Alexandre Ananoff, *L'Oeuvre Dessiné de J.-H. Fragonard,
Catalogue Raisonné*, Paris: F. de Nobele, 1961, no. 41, p. 46;
Sale catalog, *The Irma N. Straus Collection of Master
Drawings*, New York: Parke-Bernet Galleries, Inc., Oct. 21,
1970, no. 34, p. 62, repr. opp.

Portalis indicates that this drawing has had various titles in
the course of time: *La Prière au Grand-père*, 1846; *La
Prière*, 1880; *La Réprimande du Grand-papa*, 1889; and *La
Visite Chez le Docteur*, 1921-1932, according to Georges
Wildenstein.

Although chalk was the primary drawing medium of
Watteau and Boucher, Fragonard, influenced by Tiepolo,
revived the technique of drawing with ink and wash. When
he visited Italy as a young man, Fragonard was overpowered
by Michelangelo and Raphael but was able to make copies
of what he in his own words called "second-raters like
Pietro da Cortona and Giovanni Battista Tiepolo."

Of the four Hammer Fragonards the most splendid must
be considered these two drawings of children for which the
artist's young son, Alexandre-Evariste, called Fanfan, is
believed to have been the inspiration. Fragonard married
comparatively late, at the age of thirty-seven, and had two
children with his eighteen-year-old bride from his native
city of Grasse, in Provence. In these two delicious interludes,
The Little Preacher and *Grandfather's Reprimand*, the great
French artist of *l'amour*, the brilliant portrayer of the
frivolous pursuit, turned to familial themes with the same
immediacy and verve which made his work so delightful to
the Paris of his youth.

The outstanding features of these two drawings are the
broad, flowing brush strokes of the darker wash and the
light which floods the compositions with a vibrating,
dissolving intensity. Totally suffused and illuminated, the
figures themselves, despite their vigorous, broad execution
and volume, seem painted with the same airiness as the
palpitating atmosphere which surrounds them. As loose and
free as Fragonard's contemporary, Tiepolo's, graphic
technique became in its later period, Tiepolo still remained

tied to the tradition of the line. Fragonard, on the other
hand, "painted" drawings such as these over nebulous
preliminary black chalk indications.

73 Jean-Honoré Fragonard (1732-1806)
The Reading
Brown wash; the corners rounded out
11″ x 8¼″ (27.9 x 21 cm.)

Collections: H. Walferdin (Sale, Paris, Apr. 12-16, 1880, no.
192); J. P. Heseltine, London; E. H. Molyneux,
Neuilly-sur-Seine; Mrs. Jesse I. Straus, New York
(Sale, New York, Parke-Bernet Galleries, Inc., Oct. 21,
1970, no. 32)

Exhibitions: London, National Loan Exhibition, 1909-1910,
no. 99; New York: E. Gimpel and Wildenstein & Co., Inc.,
Paintings and Drawings by Fragonard, Jan. 1914, no. 31;
Paris, Musée Carnavalet, *La Vie Parisienne au XVIIIᵉᵐᵉ
Siècle*, Mar. 20-Apr. 30, 1928, no. 165; Paris, Jacques
Seligmann et Fils, Ancien Hôtel de Sagan, *Exposition de
Dessins de Fragonard, Pour la Maison Santé du Gardien
de la Paix*, May 9-30, 1931, no. 55 (lent by E. H. Molyneux);
Smithsonian Institution Traveling Exhibition Service, *The
Armand Hammer Collection*, Little Rock, Arkansas,
Arkansas Art Center, Nov. 21, 1970-Jan. 12, 1971; San
Francisco, California, California Palace of the Legion of
Honor, *The Armand Hammer Collection*, Feb. 11-Mar. 14,
1971; Oklahoma City, Oklahoma, Oklahoma Art Center,
The Armand Hammer Collection, June 15-July 11, 1971

Literature: Baron Roger Portalis, *Fragonard, Sa Vie et Son
Oeuvre*, Paris: J. Rothschild, 1889, p. 307; *Drawings by
François Boucher, J.-H. Fragonard and Antoine Watteau in
the Collection of J.P.H. (Heseltine)*, London: The Autotype
Company, 1900, no. 4, p. 39 (the engraving by Jules de
Goncourt was reproduced in place of the drawing); *Dessins
de l'Ecole Française du XVIIIᵉᵐᵉ Siècle, Provenant de la
Collection Heseltine*, Paris: Frazier-Soye, 1913, no. 32, repr.;
Catalogue of Paintings and Drawings by Fragonard, New
York: Gimpel and Wildenstein & Co., Inc., 1914, no. 31,
p. 54; Alexandre Ananoff, *L'Oeuvre Dessiné de J.-H.
Fragonard, Catalogue Raisonné*, Paris: F. de Nobele, 1961,
vol. I, no. 62, p. 55, fig. 28; Sale catalog, *The Irma N. Straus
Collection of Old Master Drawings*, New York: Parke-Bernet
Galleries, Inc., Oct. 21, 1970, no. 32, p. 58, repr. opp.

Traditionally this drawing has been held to represent
Madame Fragonard reading to her younger sister,
Marguerite Gerard, who came to live with the Fragonards
after their marriage and was not only the pupil of the
artist, but one of his favorite models. Both women were
accomplished miniaturists, and Marguerite left a fine small
portrait in oil of her celebrated brother-in-law.

Like *The Visit to the Nurse*, this drawing was originally in
the H. Walferdin Collection which was formed in Paris
during Fragonard's lifetime. Walferdin (1795-1880) was

born in the same city as Diderot and shared his admiration for Fragonard. Physician and occasional man of politics, Walferdin's true pursuits were literature and art, and he was able to acquire an exceptional group of drawings by his favorite artist.

Themes centering around letters, or the exchange of confidences, and similar *tête-à-tête* situations were popular with Fragonard's audience because they implied human drama or romance. But quieter scenes of familial intimacy were rarer in his work. *The Reading* records such a mood of quiet intimacy. The two sisters sit together, one reading to the other. The younger, drawn in profile, occupies the foreground with the volume of her full skirt, and the older is seen from the rear. The heads of the two women incline towards each other as they share a mutual involvement in the book.

The whole drawing is suffused and unified by the golden tonality of the paper. The dainty, elegant silhouette of Marguerite ranks with the happiest of Fragonard's figures in which the essential is conveyed through a minimum of details. The figures of both women are, in fact, treated more broadly here than in the identical wash drawing in the Louvre (Ananoff 61.)

74 Jean Auguste Dominique Ingres (1780-1867)
Mrs. Badham, 1816
Pencil on white wove paper:
10¼″ x 8¼″ (26.0 x 21.0 cm.)
Signed and dated lower left: J. Ingres, Del Roma 1816

Collections: Charles Badham (d. 1845); The Badham Family; C. Badham Jackson (Sale, London, Sotheby & Co., Inc., Dec. 12, 1928, no. 145, repr.); Wildenstein & Co., Inc., New York, 1929; Mrs. Jesse I. Straus, New York (Sale, New York, Parke-Bernet Galleries, Inc., Oct. 21, 1970, no. 49, repr.)

Exhibitions: New York, Paul Rosenberg Gallery, *Loan Exhibition of Ingres in American Collections*, Apr. 7-May 6, 1961, no. 22, p. 32, repr.; Cambridge, Mass., Fogg Art Museum, Harvard University, *Ingres Centennial Exhibition, 1867-1967, Drawings, Watercolors and Oil Sketches from American Collections*, Feb. 12-Apr. 9, 1967, no. 37, repr.; International Exhibitions Foundation: *Ingres in Rome*, Washington, D. C., National Gallery of Art, Jan. 23-Feb. 21, 1971, Philadelphia, Philadelphia Museum of Art, Mar. 16-Apr. 11, 1971, New York, Wildenstein & Co., Inc., Apr. 24-May 23, 1971; Smithsonian Institution Traveling Exhibition Service, *The Armand Hammer Collection*, Little Rock, Arkansas, Arkansas Art Center, Dec. 23, 1970-Jan. 12, 1971; San Francisco, California, California Palace of the Legion of Honor, Feb. 22-Mar. 14, 1971; Oklahoma City, Oklahoma, Oklahoma Art Center, *The Armand Hammer Collection*, July 23-Sept. 5, 1971

Literature: Morton D. Zabel, "Ingres in America," *The*

Arts, Feb. 1930, vol. XVI, no. 6, p. 378, repr.; Jean Cassou, "Ingres et Ses Contradictions," *Gazette des Beaux-Arts*, vol. XI, Mar. 1934, p. 157, fig. 15; Brinsley Ford, "Ingres Portrait Drawings of English People at Rome, 1806-1820," *The Burlington Magazine*, vol. LXXV, July 1939, no. 436, pp. 8 ff., pl. IIIC; Hans Naef, *Rome Vue par Ingres*, Lausanne: La Guide du Livre, 1960, p. 27, fig. 52; *Apollo*, Oct. 1970, 92:128, repr.; *Apollo*, Jan. 1971, 93:78, repr.; Sale catalog, *The Irma N. Straus Collection of Old Master Drawings*, New York: Parke-Bernet Galleries, Inc., Oct. 21, 1970, no. 49, p. 92, repr. opp.

This drawing ranks among the most enchanting made by Ingres of English visitors to Rome in the second decade of the nineteenth century. He did fewer drawings of Englishmen than of his own countrymen, but they belong to the most outstanding of his pencil portraits as exemplified, for instance, by the Los Angeles Museum's Portrait of *Thomas Church*, executed in 1816, the same year as this drawing.

In addition to her beauty, Mrs. Badham has always had a special claim to fame as the first cousin of the noted English poet, Thomas Campbell (1777-1844), author of many patriotic lyrics and related verse.

As in the Fogg Museum's double portrait of *Mrs. Vesey and Her Daughter* (Mongan-Naef, no. 36), Ingres here obviously took great delight in the details of his subject's attire, from the frills of her bonnet to her conspicuously draped Roman-striped scarf. All of these details are drawn with blunt and shaded strokes which heighten the contrast with the extremely delicate stippling of the soft face and long, slender neck, a contrast further emphasized by the dark accents of the profuse curls. In depicting all of these decorations of Mrs. Badham's person, Ingres has drawn a beguiling image of the charming feminine overdress of the early nineteenth century.

In addition to the fascinating appeal of the sitter, the off-center contrapposto position she occupies further heightens the visual interest of the composition. The artist placed her so as to provide a view of the Villa Medici and the obelisk at the top of the Spanish Steps in the background.

Mrs. Badham and her family and Ingres lived near each other on the Via Gregoriana, the same street as that portrayed here.

75 Jean François Millet (1814-1875)
Peasants Resting
Pastel: 16¾″ x 20¼″ (42.5 x 51.4 cm.)

Collections: Boussod and Valadon, Paris; Leonard Gow, Scotland; Barbizon House, London; L. M. Flesh, Piqua, Ohio (Sale, London, Sotheby & Co., July 9, 1958, no. 101, p. 21, repr.); Thomas Agnew & Sons, Ltd., London; Norton Simon, Los Angeles (Sale, New York, Parke-Bernet Galleries, Inc., May 5, 1971, no. 23, repr.)

Exhibitions: Paris, Ecole des Beaux-Arts, *Exposition Millet*, 1887, no. 96; Oklahoma City, Oklahoma, Oklahoma Art Center, *The Armand Hammer Collection*, June 15-July 11, 1971

Literature: Ecole des Beaux-Arts, *Catalogue Descriptif des Peintures, Aquarelles, Pastels, Dessins, Rehaussés, Croquis et Eaux-fortes de J.-F. Millet, au Profit de la Souscription pour Elever un Monument à la Mémoire du Maître*, Paris: Imprimerie Quantin, 1887, p. 70, no. 96, (by MM. Boussod and Valadon); *An Illustrated Record*, Barbizon House, 1937, no. 41, repr.; Sale catalog, *Highly Important 19th and 20th Century Paintings, Drawings and Sculpture, from the Private Collection of Norton Simon*, New York: Parke-Bernet Galleries, Inc., May 5, 1971, no. 23, p. 38, repr. opp. in color

The subject is a typical one for Millet—peasants resting from their labors. In this case the man uses a tinderbox to light his pipe, while the woman, seated on the ground, watches him. Moreau-Nélaton *(Millet raconté par lui-même*, Paris, 1921, vol. 3) reproduces a variant (III, fig. 223) which he dates 1866, and two pencil sketches (III, figs. 341-342) one of which (341) is clearly for this pastel. The work is known in French as *Le Briquet*, the tinder box.

76 Honoré Daumier (1808-1879)
The Pleading Lawyer
Watercolor, ink, and gouache
6¼" x 8½" (15.9 x 21.6 cm.)

Collections: Bellino (Sale, Paris, 1892, no. 32); H. P. (Sale, Paris, 1901, no. 5); Paul Gallimard, Paris; Paul Cassirer, Berlin; Jakob Goldschmidt, Berlin and New York; Alfred E. Goldschmidt, Stamford, Conn.

Exhibitions: Paris, Palais du Louvre, *Exposition de Tableaux, Statues et Objets d'Arts, au Profit de l'Oeuvre des Orphelins d'Alsace Lorraine*, 1885, no. 101 (lent by Bellino); Paris, Ecole des Beaux-Arts, *Exposition des Peintures, Aquarelles, Dessins et Lithographies des Maîtres de la Caricature, et de la Peintures de Moeurs aux XIXeme Siècle*, 1888, no. 392; Paris, Exposition Universelle, *Exposition Centennale de l'Art Français*, 1889, no. 135 (lent by Bellino); Paris, Galerie L. and P. Rosenberg, *Exposition de Dessins, Aquarelles et Lithographies de Honoré Daumier*, Apr. 15-May 6, 1907, (lent by Gallimard); St. Petersburg, *L'Art Français, Exposition Centennale*, Jan. 15-28, 1912, no. 3 (lent by Jakob Goldschmidt); Berlin, Galerie Paul Cassirer, *Ein Jahrhundert Französischer Zeichnung*, Dec. 1929-Jan. 1930, no. 17; London, Matthiesen Gallery, *A Century of French Drawings*, May 3-21, 1938, no. 39; London, Tate Gallery, The Arts Council of Great Britain, *Daumier—Paintings and Drawings*, June 14-July 30, 1961, no. 223 (lent by Mr. and Mrs. A. E. Goldschmidt); Smithsonian Institution Traveling Exhibition Service, *The Armand Hammer Collection*,

Little Rock, Arkansas, Arkansas Art Center, Nov. 21, 1970-Jan. 12, 1971; San Francisco, California, California Palace of the Legion of Honor, *The Armand Hammer Collection*, Feb. 11-Mar. 14, 1971; Oklahoma City, Oklahoma, Oklahoma Art Center, *The Armand Hammer Collection*, June 15-July 11, 1971; San Diego, California, Fine Arts Gallery of San Diego, *The Armand Hammer Collection*, July 23-Sept. 5, 1971

Literature: Ecole des Beaux-Arts, *Catalogue de l'Exposition des Peintures, Aquarelles, Dessins et Lithographies des Maîtres Français de la Caricature*, Paris: Maison Quantin, 1888 (Preface Paul Mantz), *(Gazette des Beaux-Arts)*, no. 392, p. 85; Armand Dayot, *Un Siècle d'Art, Notes sur la Peinture Française à l'Exposition Centennale des Beaux-Arts, Catalogue Complet des Oeuvres Exposées*, Paris: Librarie Plon, 1890, p. 150; René Jean, *Catalogue Commemoratif, L'Art Français à Saint-Petersbourg, Exposition Centennale*, Paris: Goupil et Cie., Manzi-Joyant et Cie., 1912, no. 3, p. 34; Erich Klossowski, *Honoré Daumier*, Munich: R. Piper Co., 1923, no. 177b, p. 102; Eduard Fuchs, *Der Maler Daumier*, New York: E. Weyhe, Leipzig: Hesse & Backer, 1927 and 1930, no. 198a, p. 54, repr. pl. 198; K. E. Maison, *Daumier Drawings*, New York and London: Thomas Yoseloff, 1960, no. 134, p. 29, repr. pl. 134; Arts Council of Great Britain, *Catalogue of an Exhibition of Daumier Paintings and Drawings at the Tate Gallery*, London: Curwen Press, 1961, no. 223, p. 67; K. E. Maison, *Honoré Daumier, Catalogue Raisonné of the Paintings, Watercolours and Drawings*, England and The Netherlands: New York Graphic Society, Ltd., 1968, vol. II, no. 675, repr. pl. 259; Sale catalog, *Important Impressionist and Modern Paintings and Drawings*, New York: Parke-Bernet Galleries, Inc., Oct. 28, 1970, no. 13, p. 24, repr. opp.

The legal profession was one which allowed Daumier the full vent of his piercing satire. He scarcely made a study of that occupation which did not expose its hypocrisy, rapacity, and stentorian oratory. At the same time, these devastating interpretations were cushioned by the artist's overriding comic sense with the result that lawyers and judges became objects of laughter rather than of derision and scorn.

The Hammer watercolor is a rare example of a Daumier interpretation of a lawyer, in that it is not risible but, on the contrary, almost sympathetic. The subject is an old, buck-toothed pleader who is shown in an intense, impassioned moment which seems to embody a life-time of courtroom behavior and to capture the timelessness of ingrained custom. Light illuminates the intent, even earnest, wrinkled face, its expression molded by constant harangue, silhouettes the semaphoric right hand, and falls sensitively on the knuckles of the other in which the brief is clasped. The head, so intensely realistic that one can almost hear the lawyer's words, is drawn with Daumier's unique lineality, composed of s-curves, arcs, parentheses, and other generally serpentine strophes, deftly but economically applied. The scene is completed with watercolor, the robes and hat heightened with gouache. Daumier fully signed the work which, although relatively small, is a highly finished masterpiece among his legal subjects.

The difficulty of arriving at an exact chronology for many of Daumier's drawings and watercolors has been pointed out repeatedly. K. E. Maison suggested that the time span between "early" and "late" works in Daumier's oeuvre may be as much as twenty-five years. A systematic or consistent evolution in the artist's drawings appear improbable, and his studies and sketches defy definite dating.

Although the Hammer drawing has not been dated by Maison, a reasonable or justifiable chronology for Daumier's large group of drawings of legal subjects may be suggested by their apparent relationship to the thirty-nine lithographs, *Le Gens de Justice*, which were printed in *Le Charivari* from 1845 to 1848. Jean Adhémar has placed many paintings, drawings, and watercolors of legal subjects in the period of 1843-1846 although he dates a spirited drawing, *Lawyer*, in the Boymans Museum as late as about 1865. Maison places a drawing, *Les deux avocats*, in 1860.

77 Eugène Boudin (1824-1898)
Beach Scene
Pencil and watercolor: 4⅝" x 9⁷/₁₆" (11.7 x 24.0 cm.)
Signed and dated lower right: Boudin 69
Inscribed lower left: Trouville

Exhibitions: Memphis, Tennessee, Brooks Memorial Art Gallery, *The Armand Hammer Collection*, Oct. 2-Dec. 30, 1969, no. 25 (repr. in cat.); Washington, D. C., Smithsonian Institution, *The Armand Hammer Collection*, Mar. 20-May 17, 1970, no. 26 (repr. in cat. in color); Smithsonian Institution Traveling Exhibition Service, *The Armand Hammer Collection*, Kansas City, Missouri, William Rockhill Nelson Gallery of Art, June 30-Aug. 2, 1970, New Orleans, Louisiana, Isaac Delgado Museum of Art, Aug. 15-Sept. 20, 1970, Columbus, Ohio, Columbus Gallery of Fine Arts, Oct. 9-Nov. 1, 1970, Little Rock, Arkansas, Arkansas Art Center, Nov. 21, 1970-Jan. 12, 1971; San Francisco, California, California Palace of the Legion of Honor, *The Armand Hammer Collection*, Feb. 11-Mar. 14, 1971; Oklahoma City, Oklahoma, Oklahoma Art Center, *The Armand Hammer Collection*, June 15-July 11, 1971; San Diego, California, Fine Arts Gallery of San Diego, *The Armand Hammer Collection*, July 23-Sept. 5, 1971

Boudin favored watercolor to give transparency to his compositions and to capture the evanescent light effects of the beaches at which he worked. The dark range of figures defining a lateral middleground against a light foreground and background (beach and sky) is typical of him. The horizontal format helps in the diffusion of focus.

This scene, like the Hammer *Beach at Trouville*, shows fashionable figures taking their ease at a popular resort.

78 Camille Pissarro (1830-1903)
Montmorency Road
Pencil: 9¼" x 12⅜" (23.5 x 31.4 cm.)
Estate stamp lower left: C.P.
Inscribed lower right: Montmorency, Enghien

Exhibitions: Memphis, Tennessee, Brooks Memorial Art Gallery, *The Armand Hammer Collection*, Oct. 2-Dec. 30, 1969; Washington, D. C., Smithsonian Institution, *The Armand Hammer Collection*, Mar. 20-May 17, 1970, no. 33 (repr. in cat. in color); Smithsonian Institution Traveling Exhibition Service, *The Armand Hammer Collection*, Kansas City, Missouri, William Rockhill Nelson Gallery of Art, June 30-Aug. 2, 1970, New Orleans, Louisiana, Isaac Delgado Museum of Art, Aug. 15-Sept. 20, 1970, Columbus, Ohio, Columbus Gallery of Fine Arts, Oct. 9-Nov. 1, 1970, Little Rock, Arkansas, Arkansas Art Center, Nov. 21, 1970-Jan. 12, 1971; San Francisco, California, California Palace of the Legion of Honor, *The Armand Hammer Collection*, Feb. 11-Mar. 14, 1971; Oklahoma City, Oklahoma, Oklahoma Art Center, *The Armand Hammer Collection*, June 15-July 11, 1971

79 Camille Pissarro (1830-1903)
Recto: *Pea Harvest*, ca. 1880
Charcoal and watercolor: 9" x 11" (22.8 x 27.9 cm.)
Signed lower right: C.P.
Verso: *Portrait of George*
Pencil and watercolor: 8½" x 11⅝" (21.6 x 29.5 cm.)

Collections: M. Knoedler & Co., Inc., New York; Mrs. Henry Gerstle, New York

Exhibitions: Memphis, Tennessee, Brooks Memorial Art Gallery, *The Armand Hammer Collection*, Oct. 2-Dec. 30, 1969, no. 31 (repr. in cat.); Washington, D. C., Smithsonian Institution, *The Armand Hammer Collection*, Mar. 20-May 17, 1970, no. 32 (repr. in cat. in color); Smithsonian Institution Traveling Exhibition Service, *The Armand Hammer Collection*, Kansas City, Missouri, William Rockhill Nelson Gallery of Art, June 30-Aug. 2, 1970, New Orleans, Louisiana, Isaac Delgado Museum of Art, Aug. 15-Sept. 20, 1970, Columbus, Ohio, Columbus Gallery of Fine Arts, Oct. 9-Nov. 1, 1970, Little Rock, Arkansas, Arkansas Art Center, Nov. 21, 1970-Jan. 12, 1971; San Francisco, California, California Palace of the Legion of Honor, *The Armand Hammer Collection*, Feb. 11-Mar. 14, 1971

Literature: Sale catalog, *Important Drawings and Watercolors of the 19th and 20th Centuries*, New York: Parke-Bernet Galleries, Inc., May 15, 1969, no. 40A, repr. opp.

80 Edouard Manet (1832-1883)
    Recto: *Man Wearing a Cloak*, 1852-1858
    Charcoal: 16″ x 8¾″ (40.6 x 19.7 cm.)
    Signed lower left with initials: ed. m.
    Verso: *Man Wearing a Cloak*
    Charcoal: 16″ x 8¾″ (40.6 x 19.7 cm.)

    Collections: Hector Brown; Arcade Gallery, London;
    Francis Cooke, Esq.; Matthiesen Gallery, London;
    Hugh Chisholm, New York

    Exhibitions: Smithsonian Institution Traveling
    Exhibition Service, *The Armand Hammer Collection*,
    Columbus, Ohio, Columbus Gallery of Fine Arts, Oct.
    9-Nov. 1, 1970, Little Rock, Arkansas, Arkansas Art
    Center, Nov. 21, 1970-Jan. 12, 1971; San Francisco,
    California, California Palace of the Legion of Honor,
    The Armand Hammer Collection, Feb. 11-Mar. 14, 1971;
    Oklahoma City, Oklahoma, Oklahoma Art Center,
    The Armand Hammer Collection, June 15- July 11, 1971

    Literature: Alain de Leiris, *The Drawings of Edouard Manet*,
    Berkeley and Los Angeles: University of California Press,
    1969, no. 135 (recto) and no. 136 (verso), repr. figs. 186,
    187; Sale catalog, *Impressionist and Modern Drawings,
    Paintings and Sculpture*, London: Christie, Manson &
    Woods, June 30, 1970, no. 1, repr.

    These monumental studies of mantled figures were drawn
    under the influence of Manet's teacher, Thomas Couture,
    who encouraged a broad style of modeling, with large
    masses of light, blocked out by straight and simplified lineal
    contouring. This approach was based on the bold
    technique used by the Italian masters of the Renaissance
    in fresco painting. Manet made many drawings after
    Renaissance artists in order to master the elements of
    design and composition. However, in the present drawings
    the glancing surfaces of light created from the reserved
    parts of the paper bespeak Manet's early interest in a
    flattening and generalizing of the form rather than in its
    strict structural volume.

81 Edgar Degas (1834-1917)
    Jacquet
    Pastel: 10¼″ x 8⅛″ (26.0 x 20.6 cm.)
    Signed center right: Degas

    Collections: Professor Hermann Heilbuth, Copenhagen;
    Bachstitz Galleries; Mrs. Jesse I. Straus, New York

    Exhibitions: Smithsonian Institution Traveling Exhibition
    Service, *The Armand Hammer Collection*; Little Rock,
    Arkansas, Arkansas Art Center, Nov. 21, 1970-Jan. 12,
    1971; San Francisco, California, California Palace of the
    Legion of Honor, *The Armand Hammer Collection*, Feb.
    11-Mar. 14, 1971; Oklahoma City, Oklahoma, Oklahoma
    Art Center, *The Armand Hammer Collection*, June 15-July

11, 1971; San Diego, California, Fine Arts Gallery of San
Diego, *The Armand Hammer Collection*, July 23-Sept.
5, 1971

Literature: *Art News*, Mar. 7, 1931, p. 5, repr.; Jean
Sutherland Boggs, *Portraits by Degas*, Berkeley and Los
Angeles: University of California Press, 1962, p. 120
(wherein the drawing is dated ca. 1878); Sales catalog,
The Irma N. Straus Collection of Old Master Drawings,
New York: Parke-Bernet Galleries, Inc., Oct. 21, 1970,
p. 94, no. 50

Degas was a master at establishing three-dimensional
volume without sacrificing a sense of the surface on which
he was working, in this case the bare paper. Of the
subject of his drawing Jean Sutherland Boggs notes
laconically "know nothing of him." At the time the work
entered the Straus Collection, however, *Art News*
identified Jacquet as Degas' frame maker. Miss Boggs dates
the portrait 1878.

82 Edgar Degas (1832-1917)
    Laundresses Carrying Linen
    Charcoal: 17″ x 23″ (43.2 x 58.4 cm.)

    Collections: Atelier Degas (4th Sale, Galerie Georges Petit,
    Paris, July 2-4, 1919, no. 357, repr.); Monsier S. . . .

    Exhibitions: Smithsonian Institution Traveling Exhibition
    Service, *The Armand Hammer Collection*, New Orleans,
    Louisiana, Isaac Delgado Museum of Art, Aug. 15-Sept.
    20, 1970, Columbus, Ohio, Columbus Gallery of Fine Arts,
    Oct. 9-Nov. 1, 1970, Little Rock, Arkansas, Arkansas Art
    Center, Nov. 21, 1970-Jan. 12, 1971; San Francisco,
    California, California Palace of the Legion of Honor,
    The Armand Hammer Collection, Feb. 11-Mar. 14, 1971;
    Oklahoma City, Oklahoma, Oklahoma Art Center,
    The Armand Hammer Collection, June 15-July 11, 1971

    Literature: Sale catalog, *Collection de Monsier S. . .* , Paris:
    Hôtel Drouot, Nov. 13, 1969, no. 20, repr. pl. III

    The softness of much of this drawing suggests that it may
    be a re-worked counterproof, probably executed rather late
    in Degas' career. The figure at the right is almost identical
    to that in the Hammer *Laundress Carrying Linen*, but
    in reverse.

83 Edgar Degas (1834-1917)
    Laundress Carrying Linen, ca. 1888-1892
    Pastel: 24″ x 36½″ (61.0 x 92.7 cm.)

    Collections: Atelier Degas (1st sale, Paris, Galerie Georges
    Petit, 1918, no. 170, repr.); Durand-Ruel, Paris:
    Henri Fèvre, Monte Carlo; Mrs. Charles R. Henschel,
    New York; Lilli Wulf, New York; Irving Vogel,
    Philadelphia; Benjamin D. Gilbert, Stamford, Conn.

Exhibitions: Paris, Galerie André Weil, *Degas, Peintre du Mouvement*, June 9-30, 1939, no. 37 (repr. p. 22); New York, Hammer Galleries, *40th Anniversary Loan Exhibition, 1928-1968*, Nov. 7-Dec. 7, 1968 (repr. in color p. 22); Memphis, Tennessee, Brooks Memorial Art Gallery, *The Armand Hammer Collection*, Oct. 2-Dec. 30, 1969, no. 33 (repr.); Washington, D. C., Smithsonian Institution, *The Armand Hammer Collection*, Mar. 20-May 17, 1970, no. 35 (repr. in cat. in color); Smithsonian Institution Traveling Exhibition Service, *The Armand Hammer Collection*, Kansas City, Missouri, William Rockhill Nelson Gallery of Art, June 30-Aug. 2, 1970, New Orleans, Louisiana, Isaac Delgado Museum of Art, Aug. 15-Sept. 20, 1970, Columbus, Ohio, Columbus Gallery of Fine Arts, Oct. 9-Nov. 1, 1970, Little Rock, Arkansas, Arkansas Art Center, Nov. 21, 1970-Jan. 12, 1971; San Francisco, California, California Palace of the Legion of Honor, *The Armand Hammer Collection*, Feb. 11-Mar. 14, 1971; Oklahoma City, Oklahoma, Oklahoma Art Center, *The Armand Hammer Collection*, June 15-July 11, 1971; San Diego, California, Fine Arts Gallery of San Diego, *The Armand Hammer Collection*, July 23-Sept. 5, 1971

Literature: Sale catalog, *Catalogue des Tableaux, Pastels et Dessins par Edgar Degas*, 1st sale, Paris: Galerie Georges Petit, 1918, p. 95, no. 170, repr.; P. A. Lemoisne, *Degas et son Oeuvre*, Paris: Paul Brame & C. M. de Hauke, 1947, vol. III, p. 559, no. 961, repr.

Degas returned to laundresses as a theme intermittently throughout his career. They offered him not the social overtones one senses in Daumier's use of the same subject, but an habitual and balanced movement. His first use of the pose appearing in this pastel, which also occurs in a charcoal drawing in the Hammer Collection, was in a painting of about 1877 (Lemoisne 410) in which it was paired with a similar figure seen from the front.

This double pose was repeated at least three times about 1902, once with horses in the background (Lemoisne 1418, 1420, 1420 bis); at the same time the single figure was also repeated against a background of horses (Lemoisne 1419). There is, finally, an almost identical pastel probably close in date to this one (Lemoisne 960). In this pastel one sees how Degas could use a figure simultaneously to render volume and to create a flat pattern activating the entire surface of the composition.

84 Edgar Degas (1834-1917)
Theater Box, 1885
Pastel: 22″ x 16½″ (56.0 x 41.0 cm.)

Collections: Atelier Degas (2nd Sale, Paris, Galerie Georges Petit, Dec. 11-13, 1918, no. 162, repr.); Mlle. Jeanne Fèvre, Nice (the artist's niece) (Sale, Paris, June 12, 1934, no. 94); Mrs. Kay, Berkshire; Reid and Léfèvre Galleries, Glasgow and London; James Archdale

Literature: Sale catalog, *Catalogue des Tableaux, Pastels et Dessins par Edgar Degas*, 2nd Sale, Paris: Galerie Georges Petit, 1918, p. 87, no. 162, repr.; Sale catalog, *Catalogue des Tableaux, Aquarelles, Pastels, Dessins, Estampes et Monotypes par Edgar Degas*, Paris: Galerie Jean Charpentier, 1934, no. 94, pl. VII, repr.; P. A. Lemoisne, *Degas et son Oeuvre*, Paris: Paul Brame and C. M. de Hauke, 1947, vol. III, p. 480, no. 829, repr.; Lillian Browse, *Degas Dancers*, New York: The Studio Publications, 1949, p. 347, no. 110, pl. 110 and frontispiece, repr. in color; Sale catalog, *Impressionist and Modern Drawings, Paintings and Sculpture*, London: Christie, Manson & Woods, 1971, p. 49, no. 48, repr. in color

Degas began fairly early in his career to use foreground audience figures as foils for more or less distant figures on stage. These figures seldom functioned as traditional *repoussoirs*, but were used as silhouettes to establish the plane of the composition. Inevitably, the middleground was dropped away and the background brought forward by the use of intense colors, obvious paint or pastel application, and complex compositional arrangements, as in this picture. Lemoisne dates this and a related composition (Lemoisne 828) to 1885 although he assigns other similar compositions to 1878-1880 (Lesmoisne 476, 577). In 1879-1880 Mary Cassatt, who was close to Degas at the time, executed several similar pictures with the auditorium rather than the stage as a background (Breeskin 61, 62, 64, 73). There is a related Degas lithograph.

85 Paul Cézanne (1839-1906)
Recto: *Study of the "Ecorché"*
Pencil: 6¼″ x 7″ (15.9 x 17.8 cm.)
Verso: *Page of Studies: The Father of the Artist*
Pencil: 10¾″ x 7″ (27.3 x 17.8 cm.)

Collections: Sir Michael Sadler, Oxford; Leicester Galleries, London; Edward Le Bas, Brighton

Exhibitions: London, Leicester Galleries, *Selection of Works from the Collection of Sir Michael Sadler*, Jan. 1944, no. 9; London, Royal Academy, *A Painter's Collection* (Edward Le Bas Coll.), Mar. 19-Apr. 28, 1963, no. 233; Memphis, Tennessee, Brooks Memorial Art Gallery, *The Armand Hammer Collection*, Oct. 2-Dec. 30, 1969; Washington, D. C., Smithsonian Institution, *The Armand Hammer Collection*, Mar. 20-May 17, 1970, no. 44 (repr. in cat. in color); Smithsonian Institution Traveling Exhibition Service, *The Armand Hammer Collection*, Kansas City, Missouri, William Rockhill Nelson Gallery of Art, June 30-Aug. 2, 1970, New Orleans, Louisiana, Isaac Delgado Museum of Art, Aug. 15-Sept. 20, 1970, Columbus, Ohio, Columbus Gallery of Fine Arts, Oct. 9-Nov. 1, 1970, Little Rock, Arkansas, Arkansas Art Center, Nov. 21, 1970-Jan. 12, 1971; San Francisco, California, California Palace of the Legion of Honor, *The Armand Hammer Collection*,

Feb. 11-Mar. 14, 1971, Oklahoma City, Oklahoma, Oklahoma Art Center, *The Armand Hammer Collection*, June 15-July 11, 1971

Literature: Sale catalog, *Impressionist and Modern Drawings, Paintings and Sculpture*, Geneva: Christie, Manson & Woods, Nov. 6, 1969, no. 154, repr.

Cézanne did a series of drawings (cf. Lionello Venturi, *Cézanne son art—son oeuvre*, Paris: Paul Rosenberg, 1936, vol. I, II, nos. 1317, 1453, 1586) and a painting (cf. Venturi no. 709) of a plaster cast. The cast was mistakenly attributed to Michelangelo in the nineteenth century and is called the "Ecorché." This recto is one of the drawings of this series.

86 Paul Cézanne (1839-1906)
Recto: *Mont Ste. Victoire*, ca. 1895
Watercolor: 6⁷/₁₆'' x 10⅝'' (16.4 x 27.0 cm.)
Verso: *Bed Post*
Pencil and watercolor: 7¼'' x 10¼'' (18.4 x 26.0 cm.)

Collections: Leicester Galleries, London; Edward Le Bas, Brighton; Sale, Geneva, Christie, Manson & Woods, Nov. 6, 1969, no. 155, repr.

Exhibitions: London, Royal Academy, *A Painter's Collection* (Edward Le Bas Coll.), Mar. 19-Apr. 28, 1963, no. 231; Scottish National Gallery of Modern Art, 1968, no. 231; Memphis, Tennessee, Brooks Memorial Art Gallery, *The Armand Hammer Collection*, Oct. 2-Dec. 30, 1969; Washington, D. C., Smithsonian Institution, *The Armand Hammer Collection*, Mar. 20-May 17, 1970, no. 43 (repr. in cat. in color); Smithsonian Institution Traveling Exhibition Service, *The Armand Hammer Collection*, Kansas City, Missouri, William Rockhill Nelson Gallery of Art, June 30-Aug. 2, 1970, New Orleans, Louisiana, Isaac Delgado Museum of Art, Aug. 15-Sept. 20, 1970, Columbus, Ohio, Columbus Gallery of Fine Arts, Oct. 9-Nov. 1, 1970, Little Rock, Arkansas, Arkansas Art Center, Nov. 21, 1970-Jan. 12, 1971; San Francisco, California, California Palace of the Legion of Honor, *The Armand Hammer Collections*, Feb. 11-Mar. 14, 1971; Oklahoma City, Oklahoma, Oklahoma Art Center, *The Armand Hammer Collection*, June 15-July 11, 1971; San Diego, California, Fine Arts Gallery of San Diego, *The Armand Hammer Collection*, July 23-Sept. 5, 1971

Literature: Sale catalog, *Impressionist and Modern Drawings, Paintings and Sculpture*, Geneva: Christie, Manson & Woods, Nov. 6, 1969, no. 155, repr.

The characteristic profile of one of Cézanne's favorite motifs is not easily discernable in this watercolor, which emphasizes the horizontal line of trees in the middle ground. Cézanne has used wash tones close to that of the paper to increase the all-over effect of the composition, an effect further enhanced by the dispersion of his accustomed broken contour.

87 Claude Monet (1840-1926)
Two Women in a Boat
Pencil on paper: 8½'' x 10⅜'' (21.6 x 26.4 cm.)

Collections: Theodore Robinson; H. Wunderlich & Co.; Mahonri Young

Exhibitions: Memphis, Tennessee, Brooks Memorial Art Gallery, *The Armand Hammer Collection*, Oct. 2-Dec. 30, 1969; Washington, D. C., Smithsonian Institution, *The Armand Hammer Collection*, Mar. 20-May 17, 1970, no. 47 (repr. in cat. in color); Smithsonian Institution Traveling Exhibition Service, *The Armand Hammer Collection*, Kansas City, Missouri, William Rockhill Nelson Gallery of Art, June 30-Aug. 2, 1970, New Orleans, Louisiana, Isaac Delgado Museum of Art. Aug. 15-Sept. 20, 1970, Columbus, Ohio, Columbus Gallery of Fine Arts, Oct. 9-Nov. 1, 1970, Little Rock, Arkansas, Arkansas Art Center, Nov. 21, 1970-Jan. 12, 1971; San Francisco, California, California Palace of the Legion of Honor, *The Armand Hammer Collection*, Feb. 11-Mar. 14, 1971; Oklahoma City, Oklahoma, Oklahoma Art Center, *The Armand Hammer Collection*, June 15-July 11, 1971

A sketch for the painting, *La Barque Bleue*, ca. 1887, of Mmes. Blanche and Jean Monet, the page is from a sketchbook of the artist.

88 Odilon Redon (1840-1916)
Vase of Flowers
Pastel: 15¾'' x 12⅜'' (40.0 x 31.4 cm.)
Signed lower right: Odilon Redon

Collection: Ruth V. McVitty, Princeton, N. J.

Exhibitions: Memphis, Tennessee, Brooks Memorial Art Gallery, *The Armand Hammer Collection*, Oct. 2-Dec. 30, 1969, no. 41 (repr. in cat.); Washington, D. C., Smithsonian Institution, *The Armand Hammer Collection*, Mar. 20-May 17, 1970, no. 48 (repr. in cat. in color); Smithsonian Institution Traveling Exhibition Service, *The Armand Hammer Collection*, Kansas City, Missouri, William Rockhill Nelson Gallery of Art, June 30-Aug. 2, 1970, New Orleans, Louisiana, Isaac Delgado Museum of Art, Aug. 15-Sept. 20, 1970, Columbus, Ohio, Columbus Gallery of Fine Arts, Oct. 9-Nov. 1, 1970, Little Rock, Arkansas, Arkansas Art Center, Nov. 21, 1970-Jan. 12, 1971; San Francisco, California, California Palace of the Legion of Honor, *The Armand Hammer Collection*, Feb. 11-Mar. 14, 1971; Oklahoma City, Oklahoma, Oklahoma Art Center, *The Armand Hammer Collection*, June 15-July 11, 1971; San Diego, California, Fine Arts Gallery of San Diego, *The Armand Hammer Collection*, July 23-Sept. 5, 1971

Literature: François Daulte, "Hammer en dix chefs-d'oeuvre," *Connaissance des Arts*, Sept. 1970, p. 80, repr.

Redon's flower pieces are at once dream-like in their disembodiment and surreal in their clarity. With no background other than the intermediate tonality of the bare paper, the colors in this work stand out with unusual sharpness from each other and from the ground. Although the ground tends to be so infinitely atmospheric as to overwhelm the vase of flowers, the composition is wholly convincing. One hardly notices, for example, that the poppies or anemones are an impossible blue.

89 Pierre Auguste Renoir (1841-1919)
Girlhood
Pencil: 13⅜″ x 11⅜″ (34.0 x 28.9 cm.)
Signed upper right: Renoir

Collection: Mrs. William Wilson, New York

Exhibitions: Paris, Galerie Charpentier, 1949, no. 282 bis; Memphis, Tennessee, Brooks Memorial Art Gallery, *The Armand Hammer Collection*, Oct. 2-Dec. 30, 1969, no. 48 (repr.); Washington, D. C., Smithsonian Institution, *The Armand Hammer Collection*, Mar. 20-May 17, 1970, no. 55 (repr. in cat. in color); Smithsonian Institution Traveling Exhibition Service, *The Armand Hammer Collection*, Kansas City, Missouri, William Rockhill Nelson Gallery of Art, June 30-Aug. 2, 1970, New Orleans, Louisiana, Isaac Delgado Museum of Art, Aug. 15-Sept. 20, 1970, Columbus, Ohio, Columbus Gallery of Fine Arts, Oct. 9-Nov. 1, 1970, Little Rock, Arkansas, Arkansas Art Center, Nov. 21, 1970-Jan. 12, 1971; San Francisco, California, California Palace of the Legion of Honor, *The Armand Hammer Collection*, Feb. 11-Mar. 14, 1971; Oklahoma City, Oklahoma, Oklahoma Art Center, *The Armand Hammer Collection*, June 15-July 11, 1971

Literature: *L'Exposition au Profit des Pauvres de la Fédération Nationale des Fils des Morts pour La France*, Paris: Galerie Charpentier, 1949, no. 282 bis.

This drawing served Renoir as the model for his drypoint *Sur la plage, à Berneval* (1892?) which Loys Delteil also used as the frontispiece for his catalog of the artist's prints in volume sixteen of *Le Peintre-Graveur Illustré*. According to Delteil, there are three states of the print. It is the last state, after the beveling of the plate, which is reproduced in his catalog.

The placement of the two girls is reversed in the print: they face towards the middle right. Figures of bathers have been added in the background.

When the third state of the print was sold at the G. Pochet sale in 1902, it was entitled *Aux Bains de Mer*.

90 Paul Gauguin (1848-1903)
Landscape at Pont-Aven
Brush and ink: 12½″ x 17¼″ (31.8 x 43.8 cm.)
Inscription lower right: No. 181

Exhibitions: Memphis, Tennessee, Brooks Memorial Art Gallery, *The Armand Hammer Collection*, Oct. 2-Dec. 30, 1969, no. 49 (repr. in cat.); Washington, D. C., Smithsonian Institution, *The Armand Hammer Collection*, Mar. 20-May 17, 1970, no. 58 (repr. in cat. in color); Smithsonian Institution Traveling Exhibition Service, *The Armand Hammer Collection*, Kansas City, Missouri, William Rockhill Nelson Gallery of Art, June 30-Aug. 2, 1970, New Orleans, Louisiana, Isaac Delgado Museum of Art, Aug. 15-Sept. 20, 1970, Columbus, Ohio, Columbus Gallery of Fine Arts, Oct. 9-Nov. 1, 1970, Little Rock, Arkansas, Arkansas Art Center, Nov. 21, 1970-Jan. 12, 1971; San Francisco, California, California Palace of the Legion of Honor, *The Armand Hammer Collection*, Feb. 11-Mar. 14, 1971; Oklahoma City, Oklahoma, Oklahoma Art Center, *The Armand Hammer Collection*, June 15-July 11, 1971; San Diego, California, Fine Arts Gallery of San Diego, *The Armand Hammer Collection*, July 23-Sept. 5, 1971

This outstanding drawing was executed during Gauguin's stay in Pont-Aven, an artists' colony on the coast of Brittany, "a land which had been little touched by Roman civilization."

According to André Schoeller, the number 181 which appears in pencil at the lower right is an indication that the drawing was once in the possession of Emile Schuffenecker (1851-1934), an artist who was Gauguin's close friend for a time at Pont-Aven. He owned several of Gauguin's drawings which were numbered in this fashion.

It was in his Brittany period, from 1886 to 1890, that Gauguin developed his style of Synthetism in which he sought to extract from the forces of nature what they inherently communicated to him rather than to represent the forms of nature's outward appearance. To accomplish this end he eschewed the traditional "sciences" of painting in favor of his own subjective response and interpretation. This led to a flattening out of forms, an over-riding of optical perspective, and a use of non-naturalistic color. During these years he was also influenced by the Art Nouveau movement as is evident from the use of the curvilinear border which divides the central motif of the drawing from the one at the extreme left and gives the composition an intriguing inner ornamental frame.

It seems possible to ascribe the drawing to the period of about 1888 based on the similarity of the house and trees with those in the painting of the same name, dated '88, now in the collection of Stavros S. Niarchos.

91 Paul Gauguin (1848-1903)
Parau No Te Varau Ino (left)
Tahitian Legend (right)
Pen, brush, and india ink; two drawings on one sheet, side by side: 6″ x 3½″ (15.2 x 8.9 cm.)

Collections: Galerie Druet, Paris; Sale, London, Sotheby & Co., Apr. 16, 1970, no. 49, p. 39, repr. opp.

Exhibitions: Smithsonian Institution Traveling Exhibition Service, *The Armand Hammer Collection*, Kansas City, Missouri, William Rockhill Nelson Gallery of Art, June 30-Aug. 2, 1970, New Orleans, Louisiana, Isaac Delgado Museum of Art, Aug. 15-Sept. 20, 1970, Columbus, Ohio, Columbus Gallery of Fine Arts, Oct. 9-Nov. 1, 1970, Little Rock, Arkansas, Arkansas Art Center, Nov. 21, 1970-Jan. 12, 1971, no. 102 (repr. in cat. supplement); San Francisco, California, California Palace of the Legion of Honor, *The Armand Hammer Collection*, Feb. 11-Mar. 14, 1971; Oklahoma City, Oklahoma, Oklahoma Art Center, *The Armand Hammer Collection*, June 15-July 11, 1971

Literature: John Rewald, *Paul Gauguin*, New York, London, and Paris: Hyperion Press, 1938 and 1949; Sale catalog, *Impressionist and Modern Drawings and Watercolors*, London: Sotheby & Co., Apr. 16, 1970, no. 49, p. 39, repr. opp.

The drawing on the left is the reverse of the woodcut *Eve* by Gauguin (Guérin 57), and it is not improbable that it is a preliminary model for the print. The woodcut was printed in an edition of thirty.

Guérin states that in the original manuscript of *Noa Noa*, Gauguin attached a photograph of a drawing representing the same figures which appear in the woodcut, but in reversed positions. The Hammer sketch may have been the one described.

Parau No Te Varau Ino is a study for the painting of the same title, meaning "words of the Devil," in the collection of Ambassador and Mrs. Averill Harriman, New York (Wildenstein no. 458).

The support of the two Hammer studies is heavy wove J. Whatman paper. Their borders indicate that they were undoubtedly intended for prints.

92   Paul Gauguin (1848-1903)
Tahitian Heads
Page from Gauguin's *Tahiti Sketchbook*
Pencil: 6⅜" x 4" (16.2 x 10.2)

Collections: Dr. Warner Muensterberger, New York; Robert Q. Lewis, Los Angeles

Exhibitions: Memphis, Tennessee, Brooks Memorial Art Gallery, *The Armand Hammer Collection*, Oct. 2-Dec. 30, 1969, no. 53 (repr. in cat.); Washington, D. C., Smithsonian Institution, *The Armand Hammer Collection*, Mar. 20-May 17, 1970, no. 59 (repr. in cat. in color); Smithsonian Institution Traveling Exhibition Service, *The Armand Hammer Collection*, Kansas City, Missouri, William Rockhill Nelson Gallery of Art, June 30-Aug. 2, 1970, New Orleans, Louisiana, Isaac Delgado Museum of Art, Aug. 15-Sept. 20, 1970, Columbus, Ohio, Columbus Gallery of Fine Arts, Oct. 9-Nov. 1, 1970, Little Rock, Arkansas, Arkansas Art Center, Nov. 21, 1970-Jan. 12, 1971;

San Francisco, California, California Palace of the Legion of Honor, *The Armand Hammer Collection*, Feb. 11-Mar. 14, 1971; Oklahoma City, Oklahoma, Oklahoma Art Center, *The Armand Hammer Collection*, June 15-July 11, 1971

Literature: Bernard Dorival (ed.), *Paul Gauguin, Carnet de Tahiti*, Paris: Quatre Chemins, 1954, no. 85

93   Paul Gauguin (1848-1903)
Pages from Sketchbook no. 16
page size 6½" x 4¼" (16.5 x 10.8 cm.)

Collection: Henri Mahaut (purchased in Cherbourg)

Exhibitions: Memphis, Tennessee, Brooks Memorial Art Gallery, *The Armand Hammer Collection*, Oct. 2-Dec. 30, 1969, nos. 50, 51, 52 (repr. in cat.); Washington, D. C., Smithsonian Institution, *The Armand Hammer Collection*, Mar. 20-May 17, 1970, no. 93 (repr. in cat. in color); Smithsonian Institution Traveling Exhibition Service, *The Armand Hammer Collection*, Kansas City, Missouri, William Rockhill Nelson Gallery of Art, June 30-Aug. 2, 1970, New Orleans, Louisiana, Isaac Delgado Museum of Art, Aug. 15-Sept. 20, 1970, Columbus, Ohio, Columbus Gallery of Fine Arts, Oct. 9-Nov. 1, 1970, Little Rock, Arkansas, Arkansas Art Center, Nov. 21, 1970-Jan. 12, 1971; San Francisco, California, California Palace of the Legion of Honor, *The Armand Hammer Collection*, Feb. 11-Mar. 14, 1971; Oklahoma City, Oklahoma, Oklahoma Art Center, *The Armand Hammer Collection*, June 15-July 11, 1971

Literature: Henri Mahaut, "Notes Synthétiques par Gauguin," *Vers et Prose*, July-Sept., 1910; John Rewald, *Gauguin*, Paris: Hyperion, 1938, boy with goose repr. p. 9; boy with pail repr. p. 8; Raymond Cogniat and John Rewald, *Paul Gauguin, a Sketchbook*, New York: Hammer Galleries, 1962 (facsimile reprint of Sketchbook No. 16, publication and translation of "Notes Synthétiques" and critical notes)

93A *Breton Peasant*
Pencil and crayon
Page 18 in Sketchbook

93B *Little Breton Boy*
Pencil and crayon
Page 19 in Sketchbook
Executed in Brittany in 1888. The same boy appears in *The Swineherd* (repr. in Georges Wildenstein, *Gauguin*, Paris: Les Beaux-Arts, 1964, vol. I, no. 255), now in the Norton Simon Collection, Los Angeles, and *The Little Breton Shepherd* (Wildenstein, op. cit. no. 256).

93C *Little Breton Boy*
Pencil and crayon
Page 20 in Sketchbook
The same boy as in 93B

93D *Bridge at Pont-Aven* (?)
Pencil and crayon
Page 26 in Sketchbook

93E *Two Breton Women*
Pencil and crayon
Page 29 in Sketchbook

93F *Head and Hand of a Monkey*
Pencil and crayon
Page 36 in Sketchbook

93G *Little Breton Boy with Goose*
Pencil and crayon
Page 37 in Sketchbook
The same boy as in 93 B and C; he also appears in
The Little Breton with Goose (Wildenstein, op. cit. no. 367)

Exhibition: Memphis, Tennessee, Brooks Memorial Art
Gallery, *The Armand Hammer Collection*, Oct. 2-Dec. 30,
1969, no. 51 (repr. in cat.)

93H *Little Breton Boy with Pail*
Pencil and crayon
Page 38 in Sketchbook
The same boy as in 93 B, C and G

Exhibition: Memphis, Tennessee, Brooks Memorial Art
Gallery, *The Armand Hammer Collection*, Oct. 2-Dec. 30,
1969, no. 52 (repr. in cat.)

93I *Little Breton Boy with Pail*
Pencil and crayon
Page 39 in Sketchbook
The same boy as in 93 B, C, G, and H

93J *Sketches of a Child*
Ink
Page 79 in Sketchbook
Cogniat (see Literature above) remarks that this child is not
a peasant, but is reminiscent of the children in the artist's
own family and in that of his Danish wife.

93K *Landscape*
Ink
Page 81 in Sketchbook

93L *Head of a Child and Self-Portrait*
Ink
Page 86 in Sketchbook
Head of child prepared for enlargement
Inscribed: Gauguin par lui-même

93M *Head of Child and Head of Man* (probably self-portrait)
Ink
Page 87 in Sketchbook

93N *Profile of Woman and Profile of Boy*
Ink
Page 95 in Sketchbook

93O *Head of Woman, Tree, and Head of Man*
Ink
Page 96 in Sketchbook
Cogniat (see Literature above) remarks that the woman may
be an Arlésienne.

93P *Self-Portrait*
Pencil
Page 111 in Sketchbook
Reminiscent of the 1885 painting, *Before the Easel*, in the
collection of Dr. Jacques Koerfer, Bern (Wildenstein, op. cit.
no. 138)

Exhibition: Memphis, Tennessee, Brooks Memorial Art
Gallery, *The Armand Hammer Collection*, Oct. 2-Dec. 30,
1969, no. 50 (repr. in cat.)

94 Vincent van Gogh (1853-1890)
Old Man Carrying a Bucket, 1822
Pencil heightened with gray and black wash
18¾" x 8¼" (47.6 x 21.0 cm.)

Collections: Ubbergen, The Netherlands; H. C. Stork,
Vienna; W. P. Maclaine Pont, Bilthoven;
Mrs. A. W. Maclaine Pont-Stork, Zwolle;
J. Donna, The Hague

Exhibitions: Smithsonian Institution Traveling Exhibition
Service, *The Armand Hammer Collection*, Columbus, Ohio,
Columbus Gallery of Fine Arts, Oct. 9-Nov. 1, 1970, Little
Rock, Arkansas, Arkansas Art Center, Nov. 21, 1970-Jan.
12, 1971; San Francisco, California, California Palace of the
Legion of Honor, *The Armand Hammer Collection*, Feb.
11-Mar. 14, 1971; Oklahoma City, Oklahoma, Oklahoma
Art Center, *The Armand Hammer Collection*,
June 15-July 11, 1971

Literature: *The Letters of Vincent van Gogh to His Brother*,
London: Constable & Co., Ltd., 1927, vol. II, Letter 251
(Dec. 4-9), pp. 40-46; J. B. de la Faille, *L'Oeuvre de Vincent
van Gogh, Catalogue Raisonné*, Paris and Brussels: Les
Editions G. van Oest, 1928, vol. III, no. 964, p. 33, vol. IV,
pl. XXXV; Dr. Walther Vanbeselaere, *De Hollandsche
Periode (1880-1885) in Het Werk van Vincent van Gogh*,
Antwerp: De Sikkel, 1937, pp. 97, 170, 208, 409; *The
Complete Letters of Vincent van Gogh* (preface Vincent W.
van Gogh, ed. Mrs. J. van Gogh-Bonger), Greenwich, Conn.:
New York Graphic Society, 1958; Letter 251, pp. 504-508;
J. B. de la Faille, *The Works of Vincent van Gogh, His
Paintings and Drawings*, Amsterdam: Meulenhoff
International, New York: Reynal & Co., with William
Morrow & Co., 1970, no. F964, pp. 360, 648, repr. p. 360;
Sale catalog, *Impressionist and Modern Watercolours,
Drawings and Bronzes*, London: Sotheby & Co., July 2,
1970, no. 20, p. 35, repr. opp. and cat. cover

95 Vincent van Gogh (1853-1890)
The Zandmennik House, ca. 1879-1880
Charcoal: 9″ x 11¾″ (22.9 x 29.8 cm.)
Signed with initials: V. G.

Collections: Decrucq, Cuesmes; M. G. Delsaut, Cuesmes;
Samuel Delsaut, Cuesmes, 1960

Exhibitions: Paris, Musée Jacquemart-André, *Vincent van
Gogh,* Feb.-Mar. 1960, no. 200, p. 56; Cuesmes, Borinage,
Vincent van Gogh, Oct. 1-20, 1960, no. 8; Smithsonian
Institution Traveling Exhibition Service, *The Armand
Hammer Collection,* Kansas City, Missouri, William
Rockhill Nelson Gallery of Art, June 30-Aug. 2, 1970, New
Orleans, Louisiana, Isaac Delgado Museum of Art, Aug.
15-Sept. 20, 1970, Columbus, Ohio, Columbus Gallery of
Fine Arts, Oct. 9-Nov. 1, 1970, Little Rock, Arkansas,
Arkansas Art Center, Nov. 21, 1970-Jan. 12, 1971, no. 104
(repr. in cat. supplement); San Francisco, California,
California Palace of the Legion of Honor, *The Armand
Hammer Collection,* Feb. 11-Mar. 14, 1971; Oklahoma City,
Oklahoma, Oklahoma Art Center, *The Armand Hammer
Collection,* June 15-July 11, 1971

Literature: Amsterdam, Stedelijk Museum, *Museum Journaal,*
series 5, no. 4, Oct. 1959, pp. 80-81, repr.; M. E. Tralbaut,
Le Mal Aimé, Lausanne: 1969, p. 63; J. B. de la Faille,
*The Works of Vincent van Gogh, His Paintings and
Drawings,* Amsterdam: Meulenhoff International, New
York: Reynal & Co. with William Morrow & Co., Inc., 1970,
no. XXXIII, p. 609; Sale catalog, *Impressionist, and Modern
Drawings, Paintings and Sculpture,* London: Christie,
Manson & Woods, Apr. 14, 1970, no. 42, p. 34, repr. opp.

96 Vincent van Gogh (1853-1890)
The Magrot House, Cuesmes, ca. 1879-1880
Charcoal: 9″ x 11¾″ (22.9 x 29.8 cm.)
Signed with initials: V. G.

Collections: Decrucq, Cuesmes; M. G. Delsaut, Cuesmes;
Samuel Delsaut, Cuesmes

Exhibitions: Paris, Musée Jacquemart-André, *Vincent van
Gogh,* Feb.-Mar. 1960, no. 199, p. 56; Cuesmes, Borinage,
Vincent van Gogh, Oct. 1-20, 1960, no. 9; Smithsonian
Institution Traveling Exhibition Service, *The Armand
Hammer Collection,* Kansas City, Missouri, William
Rockhill Nelson Gallery of Art, June 30-Aug. 2, 1970,
New Orleans, Louisiana, Isaac Delgado Museum of Art,
Aug. 15-Sept. 20, 1970, Columbus, Ohio, Columbus Gallery
of Fine Arts, Oct. 9-Nov. 1, 1970, Little Rock, Arkansas,
Arkansas Art Center, Nov. 21, 1970-Jan. 12, 1971 no. 105
(repr. in cat. supplement); San Francisco, California,
California Palace of the Legion of Honor, *The Armand
Hammer Collection,* Feb. 11-Mar. 14, 1971; Oklahoma City,
Oklahoma, Oklahoma Art Center, *The Armand Hammer
Collection,* June 15-July 11, 1971

Literature: *Museum Journaal,* series 5, no. 4, Amsterdam:
Stedelijk Museum, Oct. 1959, pp. 80-81, repr.; M. E.
Tralbaut, *Le Mal Aimé,* Lausanne: 1969, p. 63; J. B. de la
Faille, *The Works of Vincent van Gogh, His Paintings and
Drawings,* Amsterdam: Meulenhoff International, New
York: Reynal & Co. with William Morris & Co., Inc., 1970,
XXXII, p. 609; Sale catalog: *Impressionist, and Modern
Drawings, Paintings and Sculpture,* London: Christie,
Manson & Woods, Apr. 14, 1970, no. 41, p. 34, repr. opp.

97 Vincent van Gogh (1853-1890)
Man Polishing a Boot, 1882
Black chalk, pencil heightened with white and gray wash
19″ x 10½″ (48.3 x 26.7 cm.)

Collections: H. P. Bremmer, The Hague; Heirs of
H. P. Bremmer, The Hague; E. J. van Wisselingh & Co.,
Amsterdam; Mrs. J. G. ter Kuile-ter Kuile, Switzerland;
Sale, New York, Christie, Manson & Woods, Apr. 6, 1970,
no. 61, p. 46, repr. opp.

Exhibitions: Amsterdam, E. J. van Wisselingh & Co.,
*Vincent van Gogh, Aquarelles et Dessins de l'Epoque
1881-1885, Provenant de Collections Particulières
Néerlandaises,* Apr. 19-May 18, 1961, no. 19, repr.;
Smithsonian Institution Traveling Exhibition Service,
The Armand Hammer Collection, Kansas City, Missouri,
William Rockhill Nelson Gallery of Art, June 30-Aug. 2,
1970, New Orleans, Louisiana, Isaac Delgado Museum of
Art, Aug. 15-Sept. 20, 1970, Columbus, Ohio, Columbus
Gallery of Fine Arts, Oct. 9-Nov. 1, 1970, Little Rock,
Arkansas, Arkansas Art Center, Nov. 21, 1970-Jan. 12,
1971, no. 103 (repr. in cat. supplement); San Francisco,
California, California Palace of the Legion of Honor,
The Armand Hammer Collection, Feb. 11-Mar. 14, 1971;
Oklahoma City, Oklahoma, Oklahoma Art Center,
The Armand Hammer Collection, June 15-July 11, 1971

Literature: *The Letters of Vincent van Gogh to His
Brother,* London: Constable & Co., Ltd., 1927, Letter 235:
pp. 530-533, Letter 236: pp. 533-535; Letter 238:
pp. 539-543; J. B. de la Faille, *L'Oeuvre de Vincent van
Gogh, Catalogue Raisonné,* Paris and Brussels: Editions
G. van Oest, 1928, vol. III, no. 969, vol. IV, pl. XXXVII;
Dr. Walther Vanbeselaere, *De Hollandsche Periode
(1880-1885) in Het Werk van Vincent van Gogh,* Antwerp:
De Sikkel, 1937, pp. 88, 91, 170, 190, 409; *Letters to an
Artist: from Vincent van Gogh to Anton Ridder van
Rappard, 1881-1885* (trans. Rela van Messel, intro.
Walter Pach), New York: Viking Press, 1937, p. 48; *Letters
de van Gogh à van Rappard* (trans. L. Roelandt), Paris:
Bernard Grasset, 1950; *The Complete Letters of Vincent
van Gogh* (preface Vincent W. van Gogh, ed. Mrs. J. van
Gogh-Bonger), Greenwich, Conn: New York Graphic
Society, 1958, Letter 235: pp. 463-466; Letter 236:
pp. 466-467; Letter 238: pp. 470-473; J. B. de la Faille,

The Works of Vincent van Gogh, His Paintings and Drawings, Amsterdam: Meulenhoff International, New York: Reynal & Co. with William Morrow & Co., Inc., 1970, no. F969, pp. 361, 648, repr. p. 361; Sale catalog, *Impressionist, American and Modern Paintings and Watercolors*, Houston, Texas: Christie, Manson & Woods (New York), Apr. 6, 1970, no. 61, p. 46, repr. opp.

A great artist's student or formative work, when present, is always pertinent as a means of assessing the magnitude of his development, and very rarely has that development been as marked as in the case of van Gogh's drawing style.

The two Hammer Collection studies of cottages date from 1879-1880; the two studies of workers date from The Hague period, December 1881 to September 1883. The four thus show van Gogh's early works, from his twenty-sixth to his thirtieth year. Homely, primitive, "amateurish," they are among his first earnest efforts to portray the poor and humble—old men at their daily tasks and simple cottages of country folk—and they furnish a revealing contrast to his subsequent progress.

Within the next two years van Gogh advanced to a remarkable level of drawing which went far beyond his first stiff and crude essays. The hard, rude lines and general awkwardness gave way to a powerful command of *graphisme*, particularly in his peasant studies. His modeling became free, bold, and decisive, his forms broad and monumental. Van Gogh's vigorous treatment of the laboring figure in all of its tension far surpassed the treatment of similar subjects in the drawings of Millet, who had been one of his central inspirations.

98 Vincent van Gogh (1853-1890)
The Weaver, ca. 1884
Watercolor, 12½" x 17¾" (31.8 x 45.1 cm.)

Collections: Galerie Druet, Paris; Georges Gérard, Limoges: Galerie Druet, Paris; Mrs. G. Guibert, Limoges; Heirs of Mrs. Guibert (Sale, Paris, Palais Galliéra, June 20, 1968, no. 225; Drs. Fritz and Peter Nathan, Zurich

Exhibitions: Washington, D. C., Smithsonian Institution, *The Armand Hammer Collection*, Mar. 20-May 17, 1970; Smithsonian Institution Traveling Exhibition Service, *The Armand Hammer Collection*, Kansas City, Missouri, William Rockhill Nelson Gallery of Art, June 30-Aug. 2, 1970, New Orleans, Louisiana, Isaac Delgado Museum of Art, Aug. 15-Sept. 20, 1970, Columbus, Ohio, Columbus Gallery of Fine Arts, Oct. 9-Nov. 1, 1970, Little Rock, Arkansas, Arkansas Art Center, Nov. 21, 1970-Jan. 12, 1971, no. 107 (repr. in catalog supplement); San Francisco, California, California Palace of the Legion of Honor, *The Armand Hammer Collection*, Feb. 11-Mar. 14, 1971; Oklahoma City, Oklahoma, Oklahoma Art Center, *The Armand Hammer Collection*, June 15-July 11, 1971

Literature: J. B. de la Faille, *L'Oeuvre de Vincent van Gogh, Catalogue Raisonné*, Paris and Brussels: Editions G. van Oest, 1928, vol. III, no. 1108, vol. IV, pl. LXX; Dr. Walther Vanbeselaere, *De Hollandsche Periode (1880-1885) in Het Werk van Vincent van Gogh*, Antwerp: De Sikkel, 1937, pp. 257, 317, 410; *Lettres de Vincent van Gogh à son Frere, Théo* (trans. George Philippart, preface Charles Terrasse), Paris: Editions Bernard Grasset, 1937, Letter 351, pp. 103-104; *Vincent van Gogh, Brieven aan Zijn Broeder*, J. van Gogh-Bonger, Amsterdam: 1914, Letter 351, vol. II, p. 383; *The Complete Letters of Vincent van Gogh* (ed. Mrs. J. van Gogh-Bonger, preface Vincent W. van Gogh), Greenwich, Connecticut: New York Graphic Society, Letter 351, vol. II, p. 249; J. B. de la Faille, *The Works of Vincent van Gogh, His Paintings and Drawings*, Amsterdam: Meulenhoff International, New York: Reynal & Co. with William Morrow & Co., Inc., 1970, no. F1108, pp. 406, 652, repr. p. 406

Workers were among the favorite themes of van Gogh's Nuenen years (1883-1885), and weavers seem particularly to have intrigued him during the late winter and spring of 1884. At that time he wrote to Theo, "Do you know many drawings of weavers? I know only a very few. I began by making three water colors of them . . . they are but poor creatures, those weavers." The tonality and application of the watercolor in this work show what Vincent owed to Mauve and the Hague school. There is a closely related painting (de la Faille 162).

99 Henri-Edmond Cross (1856-1910)
Cypresses, 1896
Gouache: 9½" x 13¼" (24.1 x 33.7 cm.)

Collections: William J. Holliday, Indianapolis; Modern Art Foundation, Geneva; Pierre Matisse Gallery, New York

Exhibitions: Cleveland Museum of Art, *Tenth Exhibition of Watercolors and Pastels*, Jan. 10-Feb. 12, 1933; Memphis, Tennessee, Brooks Memorial Art Gallery, *The Armand Hammer Collection*, Oct. 2-Dec. 30, 1969, no. 55 (repr. in cat.); Washington, D. C., Smithsonian Institution, *The Armand Hammer Collection*, Mar. 20-May 17, 1970, no. 61 (repr. in cat. in color); Smithsonian Institution Traveling Exhibition Service, *The Armand Hammer Collection*, Kansas City, Missouri, William Rockhill Nelson Gallery of Art, June 30-Aug. 2, 1970, New Orleans, Louisiana, Isaac Delgado Museum of Art, Aug. 15-Sept. 20, 1970, Columbus, Ohio, Columbus Gallery of Fine Arts, Oct. 9-Nov. 1, 1970, Little Rock, Arkansas, Arkansas Art Center, Nov. 21, 1970-Jan. 12, 1971; San Francisco, California, California Palace of the Legion of Honor, *The Armand Hammer Collection*, Feb. 11-Mar. 14, 1971; Oklahoma City, Oklahoma, Oklahoma Art Center, *The Armand Hammer Collection*, June 15-July 11, 1971

Literature: Isabelle Compin, *H. E. Cross*, Paris: Quatre Chemins, 1964, repr. pp. 146, 338

Miss Compin reproduces an oil, 25½″ x 36¼″, of the identical image, entitled *Nocturne*, painted in 1896 and now in the collection of M. O. Ghez, Geneva. She also reproduces a four-color lithograph, 11⅛″ x 16⅛″, published by Vollard in 1896 as *La Promenade*. Miss Compin believes she may have found the source of the subject in a play of 1892 by Edouard Dujardin. In the play, *Le Chevalier Passé*, Act III, Scene I, night is falling and the four Floramyes, preparing to leave the isle of Antonia, lament: "Adieu, les rives où nous avons vécu! Adieu, les charmants bords où nos songes longtemps ne sont plus!"

100 Georges Seurat (1859-1891)
Study after 'The Models,' 1888
Pen and ink: 10¹/₁₆″ x 6⅜″ (26.0 x 16.5 cm.)
Signed lower left: Seurat

Collections: Emile Seurat, Paris; Alexandre Natanson, Paris; Galerie Bolette Natanson, Paris; Jean-Charles Moreux, Paris; Mme. Jean-Charles Moreux, Paris; Wildenstein & Co., Inc., New York; Norton Simon, Los Angeles

Exhibitions: Paris, La Revue Blanche, *Seurat*, Mar. 19-Apr. 5, 1900 (hors. cat.); Paris, Galerie Bernheim-Jeune, *Rétrospective Georges Seurat*, Dec. 14, 1908-Jan. 9, 1909, no. 197; Paris, Galerie Bernheim-Jeune, *Les Dessins de Seurat*, Nov. 29-Dec. 24, 1926, no. 114; London, Galerie Syrie Maugham, Bolette Natanson, *Seurat*, May 21-June 7, 1935; Paris, Galerie Paul Rosenberg, *Georges Seurat*, Feb. 3-29, 1936, no. 130, suppl.; Paris, Galerie Bolette Natanson, "Les Cadres," *Peintres de la Revue Blanche*, 1936, no. 50, suppl.; Paris, Musée Jacquemart-André, *Seurat*, Nov.-Dec. 1957, no. 55; Oklahoma City, Oklahoma, Oklahoma Art Center, *The Armand Hammer Collection*, June 15-July 11, 1971

Literature: Paul Adam, "Les Impressionistes à l'Exposition des Indépendants," *La Vie Moderne*, Paris, Apr. 15, 1888, p. 229, repr.; André Lhote, *Georges Seurat*, Rome: Editions de Valori Plastici, Coll. "Les Artistes Nouveaux," 1922, p. II, repr.; Florent Fels, "Les Dessins des Georges Seurat," *L'Amour de l'Art*, no. I, Paris, Jan., 1927, p. 43, repr.; Gustave Kahn, *Les Dessins de Georges Seurat*, Paris: Editions Bernheim-Jeune, 1928, pl. 98, repr.; Waldemar George, *Seurat et le Divisionnisme*, Paris: Editions Librairie de France, Coll. "Les Albums d'Art Druet," 1928, p. 15, repr.; Thadée Natanson, "Sur Une Exposition des Peintres de la Revue Blanche," *Arts et Métiers Graphiques*, no. 54, Paris, Aug. 15, 1936, p. 16, repr.; Robert J. Goldwater, "Some Aspects of the Development of Seurat's Style," *The Art Bulletin*, vol. XXIII, no. 2, New York: Wittenborn & Co., 1946, no. 80, p. 104, repr.; Henri Dorra and John Rewald, *Seurat, L'Oeuvre Peint,*

Biographie et Catalogue Critique, Paris: Les Beaux-Arts, Editions d'Etudes et de Documents, 1959, no. 179a, p. 222, repr.; C. M. de Hauke, *Seurat et Son Oeuvre*, Paris: Gründ, 1961, vol. II, no. 665, p. 254, repr.; Sale catalog, *Highly Important 19th and 20th Century Paintings, Drawings and Sculpture, from the Private Collection of Norton Simon*, New York: Parke-Bernet Galleries, Inc., May 5, 1971, no. 46, p. 88, repr. opp.

According to Dorra-Rewald, this is a copy made by the artist after the central figure in his painting, *The Models*. Created to serve as an illustration for the review, *La Vie Moderne*, it appeared in the issue of April 15, 1888.

Seurat was rarely active as an illustrator or poster artist. He is known to have provided a cover for a novel by Victor Jose, a writer for whose works Toulouse-Lautrec executed several posters.

To be noted in this line drawing is the complete alteration of the expression of the original model's face.

101 Henri de Toulouse-Lautrec (1864-1901)
Dance at the Moulin de la Galette, 1889
Ink and blue crayon on buff paper, heightened with white
33½″ x 37½″ (85.1 x 95.3 cm.)
Signed lower right: T. Lautrec

Collections: Galerie Thannhauser, Berlin; Pierre Decourcelle, Paris (Sale, June 16, 1926, no. 72); James W. Barney, New York; M. Knoedler & Co., Inc., New York; Mrs. Edward Hutton, Westbury, Long Island (Sale, London, Sotheby & Co., July 1, 1964, no. 20, repr. in color); O'Hana Gallery, London; Mr. and Mrs. Roy C. Markus, Los Angeles

Exhibitions: Paris, Hôtel Charpentier, *Exposition de la Musique et de la Danse*, 1923, no. 103, and *Fraternité des Artistes*, 1926; New Haven, Yale University Art Gallery, 1930; The Art Institute of Chicago, *Loan Exhibition of Paintings, Drawings, Prints and Posters by Henri de Tolouse-Lautrec*, Dec. 1930-Jan. 1931, no. 42 (lent by James W. Barney); New York, Museum of Modern Art, *Lautrec-Redon*, 10th Loan Exhibition, Feb.-Mar. 1931, no. 38; Washington, D. C., Smithsonian Institution, *The Armand Hammer Collection*, Mar. 20-May 17, 1970, no. 65 (repr. in cat. in color); Smithsonian Institution Traveling Exhibition Service, *The Armand Hammer Collection*, Kansas City, Missouri, William Rockhill Nelson Gallery of Art, June 30-Aug. 2, 1970, New Orleans, Louisiana, Isaac Delgado Museum of Art, Aug. 15-Sept. 20, 1970, Columbus, Ohio, Columbus Gallery of Fine Arts, Oct. 9-Nov. 1, 1970, Little Rock, Arkansas, Arkansas Art Center, Nov. 21, 1970-Jan. 12, 1971; San Francisco, California, California Palace of the Legion of Honor, *The Armand Hammer Collection*, Feb. 11-Mar. 14, 1971; Oklahoma City, Oklahoma, Oklahoma Art Center, *The Armand Hammer Collection*, June 15-July 11, 1971

Literature: *Courrier Français*, May 19, 1889, p. 11; Maurice Joyant, *Henri de Toulouse-Lautrec*, Paris: H. Floury, 1926, vol. II, p. 193; Sale catalog, *French Nineteenth and Twentieth Century Paintings and Drawings, The Property of Mrs. Edward Hutton of Westbury, Long Island*, London: Sotheby & Co., July 1, 1964, no. 20, repr. in color

The drawing was made by Toulouse-Lautrec after the painting of the same subject now in the Art Institute of Chicago for publication in the *Courrier Français*, no. 20, May 19, 1889, p. 11. The man in the bowler hat is the painter Joseph Albert.

102   Pierre Bonnard (1867-1947)
Girl Drying Her Knees
Pencil: 13″ x 9½″ (33.0 x 24.1 cm.)
Signed lower right: Bonnard

Exhibitions: Memphis, Tennessee, Brooks Memorial Art Gallery, *The Armand Hammer Collection*, Oct. 2-Dec. 30, 1969, no. 61 (repr. in cat.); Washington, D. C., Smithsonian Institution, *The Armand Hammer Collection*, Mar. 20-May 17, 1970, no. 68 (repr. in cat. in color); Smithsonian Institution Traveling Exhibition Service, *The Armand Hammer Collection*, Kansas City, Missouri, William Rockhill Nelson Gallery of Art, June 30-Aug. 2, 1970, New Orleans, Louisiana, Isaac Delgado Museum of Art, Aug. 15-Sept. 20, 1970, Columbus, Ohio, Columbus Gallery of Fine Arts, Oct. 9-Nov. 1, 1970, Little Rock, Arkansas, Arkansas Art Center, Nov. 21, 1970-Jan. 12, 1971; San Francisco, California, California Palace of the Legion of Honor, *The Armand Hammer Collection*, Feb. 11-Mar. 14, 1971; Oklahoma City, Oklahoma, Oklahoma Art Center, *The Armand Hammer Collection*, June 15-July 11, 1971

103   Pablo Picasso (1881-   )
Recto: *Female Nude*
Pencil: 6½″ x 4″ (16.5 x 10.2 cm.)

Signed upper right: Picasso
Verso: *Young Man*, ca. 1906
Pen and ink: 6½″ x 4″ (16.5 x 10.2 cm.)
Signed lower right: Picasso

Collections: Saidenberg Gallery, New York; George Axelrod, New York

Exhibitions: Smithsonian Institution Traveling Exhibition Service, *The Armand Hammer Collection*, Kansas City, Missouri, William Rockhill Nelson Gallery of Art, June 30-Aug. 2, 1970, New Orleans, Louisiana, Isaac Delgado Museum of Art, Aug. 15-Sept. 20, 1970, Columbus, Ohio, Columbus Gallery of Fine Arts, Oct. 9-Nov. 1, 1970, Little Rock, Arkansas, Arkansas Art Center, Nov. 21, 1970-Jan. 12, 1971, no. 112 (repr. in cat. supplement); San Francisco, California, California Palace of the Legion of Honor, *The Armand Hammer Collection*, Feb. 11-Mar. 14, 1971; Oklahoma City, Oklahoma, Oklahoma Art Center, *The Armand Hammer Collection*, June 15-July 11, 1971

Literature: Sale catalog, *Impressionist and Modern Drawings and Watercolours*, London: Sotheby & Co., Apr. 16, 1970, no. 92, pp. 118-119, repr.

This double-sided drawing belongs to the period of about 1906, and the female nude incorporates many of the "classicizing" features which Picasso adopted at that time. His work became simplified, more abstract and sculptural. The face with its far-off gaze is delineated with a minimum of lines and accords with various other "mask-like" portraits of the period. But the relatively broad, squat body, treated in summary fashion, reflects some of the quality of the late Iberian sculpture which was another factor in Picasso's earlier work.

That the verso sketch is so close to being a caricature suggests that it may have been drawn of a friend, perhaps at a cafe. An earlier sketch of roughly the same type, in which the man leans his arm on a cafe table, was formerly in the Galerie Rosengart in Lucerne, Switzerland.

Index of Artists

Bernard, Emile
32 *Wheat Harvest*

Bonnard, Pierre
102 *Girl Drying Her Knees*
39 *Nude against the Light*
38 *Street Scene*

Boucher, François
69 *Landscape with a Rustic Bridge*
68 *Venus Reclining against a Dolphin*

Boudin, Eugène
16 *Beach at Trouville*
77 *Beach Scene*
15 *Quay at Camaret*
14 *Sailing Ships in Port*

Caillebotte, Gustave
17 *Square in Argenteuil*

Cassatt, Mary
56 *Reine Lefebvre and Margot*
57 *Summertime*

Cézanne, Paul
30 *Boy Resting*
86 *Mont Ste. Victorie*
85 *Study of the "Ecorché"* (recto)
Page of Studies: The Father of the Artist (verso)

Chagall, Marc
50 *Blue Angel*

Corot, Camille
11 *Grape Harvest at Sèvres*
9 *Harvester Under Trees*
10 *Distant View of Mantes Cathedral*
8 *Medieval Ruins*
12 *Morning*
13 *Pleasures of Evening*
7 *Portrait of a Girl*

Correggio, Antonio Allegri da
62 *Pendentive Study with Sts. Matthew and Jerome* (recto)
Study for the "Madonna della Scodella" (verso)

Cross, Henri-Edmond
99 *Cypresses*

Daumier, Honoré
76 *The Pleading Lawyer*

Degas, Edgar
81 *Jacquet*
83 *Laundress Carrying Linen*
82 *Laundresses Carrying Linen*
84 *Theater Box*
27 *Three Dancers in Yellow Skirts*

Derain, André
44 *Still Life with Basket, Jug and Fruit*

Dongen, Kees van
48 *Friends*

Dürer, Albrecht
60 *Tuft of Cowslips*

Eakins, Thomas
55 *Portrait of Sebastiano Cardinal Martinelli*

Fantin-Latour, Henri
24 *Peonies in a Blue and White Vase*
25 *Portrait of Miss Edith Crowe*
26 *Roses*

Fragonard, Jean-Honoré
4 *The Education of the Virgin*
72 *Grandfather's Reprimand*
71 *The Little Preacher*
73 *The Reading*
70 *Visit to the Nurse*

Gauguin, Paul
33 *Bonjour M. Gauguin*
91 *Parau No Te Varau Ino* (left)
Tahitian Legend (right)
90 *Landscape at Pont-Aven*
93a-p *Sketchbook No. 16*
92 *Tahitian Heads*

Géricault, Théodore
6 *Portrait of a Gentleman*

Gogh, Vincent van
34 *Garden of the Rectory at Nuenen*
37 *Hospital at Saint-Rémy*
35 *Lilacs*
96 *The Magrot House, Cuesmes*
97 *Man Polishing a Boot*
94 *Old Man Carrying a Bucket*
36 *The Sower*
98 *The Weaver*
95 *The Zandemennik House*

Goya, Francisco
5 *El Pelele*

Harnett, William Michael
52 *Still Life*

Ingres, Jean Auguste Dominique
74 *Mrs. Badham*

Laurencin, Marie
49 *Women in the Forest*

Manet, Edouard
80 *Man Wearing a Cloak* (recto)
Man Wearing a Cloak (verso)

Millet, Jean François
75 *Peasants Resting*

Modigliani, Amedeo
45 *Woman of the People*

Monet, Claude
87 *Two Women in a Boat*
19 *View of Bordighera*

Moreau, Gustave
28 *King David*
29 *Salome*

Picasso, Pablo
103 *Female Nude* (recto)
Young Man (verso)

Pissarro, Camille
23 *Boulevard Montmartre, Mardi Gras*
78 *Montmorency Road*
79 *Pea Harvest*

Prendergast, Maurice Brazil
58 *On the Beach*

Raphael Sanzio
61 *Study for a Fresco with Hosea and Jonah*

Redon, Odilon
88 *Vase of Flowers*

Rembrandt van Rijn
63 *A Biblical Subject*
1 *Portrait of a Man of the Raman Family*

Renoir, Pierre Auguste
21 *Antibes*
89 *Girlhood*

Renoir, Pierre Auguste
22 *Grapepickers at Lunch*
20 *Two Girls Reading*

Rouault, Georges
47 *Circus Girl*

Rubens, Peter Paul
3   *The Israelites Gathering Manna
    in the Desert*
2   *Young Woman with Curly Hair*

Sargent, John Singer
53 *Dr. Pozzi at Home*
54 *Portrait of Mrs. Edward L. Davis
    and Her Son, Livingston Davis*

Seurat, Georges
100 *Study after 'The Models'*

Sisley, Alfred
18 *Timber Yard at Saint-Mammès*

Stuart, Gilbert
51 *Portrait of George Washington*

Tiepolo, Giovanni Battista
67 *St. Jerome in the Desert
    Listening to the Angels*
66 *Virgin and Child Adored
    by Bishops, Monks, and Women*

Toulouse-Lautrec, Henri de
101 *Dance at the Moulin de la Galette*
31 *In the Salon*

Vlaminck, Maurice de
46 *Summer Bouquet*

Vuillard, Edouard
42 *At the Seashore*
40 *In the Bus*
43 *Interior*
41 *Rue Lepic, Paris*

Watteau, Jean Antoine
65 *Couple Seated on a Bank*
64 *Young Girl*

Wyeth, Andrew
59 *Brandywine Valley*

The catalog was designed in Los Angeles by James L. Wood
All text was set in Aldus by Grant Dahlstrom/The Castle Press,
Pasadena, and the catalog printed on 100 lb. Cameo by
Anderson Lithograph Company, Los Angeles